A
HORACE
Workbook

Latin Literature Workbook Series

A Series Edited by LeaAnn A. Osburn

A
HORACE
Workbook

David J. Murphy
& Ronnie Ancona

Bolchazy-Carducci Publishers, Inc.
Wauconda, Illinois USA

Series Editor
LeaAnn A. Osburn

Volume Co-Editors
LeaAnn A. Osburn
Donald E. Sprague

Typography, Page and Cover Design
Adam Phillip Velez

A Horace Workbook

by David J. Murphy & Ronnie Ancona

Bolchazy-Carducci Publishers, Inc.
1000 Brown Street
Wauconda, IL 60084 USA
www.bolchazy.com

Printed in the United States of America
2005
by United Graphics

ISBN-13: 978-0-86516-574-8
ISBN-10: 0-86516-574-2

CONTENTS

FOREWORD

All Latin teachers want their students to read ancient authors in the original. Yet to study the authentic Latin of an ancient Roman author is a complex task. It requires comprehension of the text and its grammatical underpinnings; an understanding of the world events and the culture in which the work of literature was produced; an ability to recognize the figures of speech the author uses and to grasp the impact they have on the text; sensitivity to the way sound effects, including meter if a passage is poetry, interact with the meaning of the text; and the ability to probe whatever thoughts and ideas the author may be expressing. To be successful in this multifaceted task, students need not only a comprehensive textbook but also exercises of different kinds in which to practice their newly developing literary and critical skills.

Students often need extensive drill and practice material—something not available in the traditional Latin author textbook—to help them master the grammar and syntax of the Latin text as well as the literary skills that the text demands of its readers. Teachers, too, no matter how many questions they ask in class to help their students analyze the syntax and the literary qualities of the text, often need and want more questions to be available. Realizing this need on the part of both students and teachers, Bolchazy-Carducci Publishers has begun to develop a series of workbooks to accompany Advanced Placement textbooks. There will be five workbooks in the series, one for each advanced placement author: Catullus, Cicero, Horace, Ovid, and Vergil. A team of authors—one, a university scholar with special expertise in the Latin literary text and the other, a high school Advanced Placement Latin teacher—will write each workbook.

Workbooks in this series will contain the Latin text for the material on the Advanced Placement Syllabus and exercises that drill grammar, syntax, and figures of speech. In addition, multiple-choice questions will be included and will focus on the student's comprehension of the passage and on items of literary analysis. The workbooks will also feature scansion practice, essays to write, and other questions that are appropriate to the author being studied. By reading and answering these types of questions, students will gain experience with the types of questions that are found on the Advanced Placement Examinations. Students at the college level will also benefit from the additional practice offered in the workbooks.

These workbooks contain neither textual notes nor vocabulary on the page with the text nor on the facing page. The absence of these traditional features of textbooks will allow students, after reading the Latin passage in the textbook, to practice in the workbook what they have learned and to assess how much they have mastered already and what needs more study. The workbooks will, however, contain a Latin to English Vocabulary at the back of the book.

We are confident that this series of workbooks has a unique role to play in fostering students' understanding of authentic Latin text and will be a significant addition to the Advanced Placement and college materials that already exist.

LeaAnn A. Osburn
Series Editor

PREFACE

We are grateful to Bolchazy-Carducci Publishers for giving us the opportunity to collaborate on *A Horace Workbook,* one in the series of workbooks planned for Advanced Placement Latin authors. The challenge of devising exercises to help students understand and write about Horace has been a most enjoyable one. We had already worked together on Horace in the past when Ronnie Ancona visited David Murphy's Latin Literature AP* class to discuss her work on Horace *Ode* 1.23 (the "Chloe Ode") and when Murphy was a peer reviewer of the Teacher's Guide to Ancona's *Horace: Selected Odes and Satire 1.9* for Bolchazy-Carducci Publishers. This project has allowed us to extend that earlier common engagement with Horace. With one of us teaching high school and the other college, we have shared differing perspectives to our benefit. Of course, one always profits by testing one's ideas against another, informed mind. That endeavor was all the more rewarding in this case, for it was accompanied by shared sensibilities, goals, and respect. We hope we have produced a workbook that will enhance students' reading of Horace. Its writing was a pleasure for the authors.

This workbook is designed to provide high school and college students with exercises to accompany their reading in Latin of selected poems of Horace. It provides extensive practice with the Latin, which will develop and reinforce the students' skills in a variety of ways. The audience for which the book is intended is the Advanced Placement Horace student or the college level student of Horace who is reading the Horace poems that appear on the AP* syllabus. The workbook can be used in conjunction with any textbook or edition of Horace. The text printed and the Latin Vocabulary included are those of Ronnie Ancona, *Horace: Selected Odes and Satire 1.9* (Wauconda, Il.: Bolchazy-Carducci Publishers, 1999, second edition, 2005).

For each poem we provide the following types of exercises:

I.   Short Answer Questions

II.   Multiple Choice Questions

III.   Translation

IV.   Short Analysis Questions

V.   Essay

VI.   Scansion

II–V are similar to questions found on the Latin Advanced Placement Examinations. For these, we suggest time limits in line with those suggested for similar questions on the AP Exam. We do not suggest time limits for I and VI, since they provide needed practice but are not patterned after types of questions used on the AP Exam.

---

*   AP is a registered trademark of the College Entrance Examination Board, which was not involved in the production of, and does not endorse, this product.

I. Short Answer Questions

These questions ask, in line-by-line order, for analysis of grammatical or syntactical points (e.g. case and use of nouns), identification of figures of speech, and translation of words or phrases. They can be completed by students working alone, in pairs or groups, or together as a class "advancing the text at sight." This exercise is particularly useful for the student who is translating the poem for the first time.

A note on terminology—when we ask for the "function" of a word, the student's task is to explain the word's grammatical or syntactical use in its context. For example, on *Ode 1.24.9*, we ask "what is the case and use of *bonis*, and what is its function?" The answer would be, "dative of reference with *flebilis*; adjective used as a substantive."

II. Multiple Choice Questions

These questions ask about the same features as the multiple-choice questions on the Advanced Placement Examination: translation or interpretation, grammar, lexical details, allusions or references, metrics, and figures of speech. Each exercise concerns a passage of up to sixteen lines.

As currently constituted, the multiple-choice section of the Latin Literature Advanced Placement Exam consists of four passages: three "unseen" passages (usually one prose and two poetry) and one "seen" passage from the Catullus syllabus. On the Advanced Placement Exam, students do not encounter multiple-choice questions on poems from the Horace syllabus. Nevertheless, we have included a multiple-choice exercise for each poem because students generally find multiple-choice AP* questions difficult, and they profit from extensive practice.

We intend the multiple-choice questions for students who have already translated the poem. Their degree of difficulty resembles that of Advanced Placement multiple-choice questions on passages of Catullus that students have read. For that reason, our suggested time is shorter than what is allowed on the Advanced Placement Exam for the same number of questions on an "unseen" passage. Teachers who want to give our multiple-choice exercises to students who have not yet read the passage should supply unfamiliar vocabulary and allow at least 1.2 minutes per question.

Finally, in the Appendix we provide students with four practice multiple-choice exercises, with answers, on "unseen" passages to add to their experience with this type of exercise.

III. Translation

These exercises test translation skills of students who have already translated the poem. Passages are of approximately the same length as translation passages on the Advanced Placement Exam. The directions call for a translation that is as literal as possible. For that reason, one should not switch active voice verbs to passive voice or vice versa, or alter verb tenses. In rendering the historical present, one should either use the English present tense for Latin present or convert to past tense in English consistently. Students should stay within the range of accepted definitions of words and not impose from context a sense that the word does not have.

IV. Short Analysis Questions

These questions, similar to what have informally been called "spot" questions on the Advanced Placement Exam, ask the student to address several detailed issues in a passage: translation, interpretation, scansion, analysis of figurative language, identification of historical or literary allusions. They are designed for students who have already read/translated the poem. Having discussed it already in class is helpful as well.

---

* AP is a registered trademark of the College Entrance Examination Board, which was not involved in the production of, and does not endorse, this product.

V. Essay

Aimed at students who have already read/translated and discussed the poem in class, the essay questions call for in-depth analysis of a feature of a passage or entire poem. The grading scheme suggested in the Teacher's Guide evaluates responses on a scale of 0–6.

The essay should:

- address the question exactly as it is asked, especially if it entails more than one task
- analyze, not merely describe, the passage so as to answer the question
- address the passage as a whole
- support assertions with evidence from the Latin. This means copy the Latin or cite the line numbers AND translate or paraphrase closely enough that it is clear the Latin is understood.

VI. Scansion

Once they have learned its meter, students can practice scansion from a poem whether or not they have translated it. Following the format of the Advanced Placement Exam, we do not provide macrons/long marks in the lines to be scanned.

A Word on Figures of speech

In this workbook, we use the term "figure of speech" to refer to figurative uses of language in general, whether they involve non-standard senses of words (tropes or figures of thought) or arrangements of words (rhetorical figures or figures of speech). We use the term in this broad sense to encompass not only all the literary devices that are designated "figures of speech" to be learned for the Advanced Placement Examination, but also some devices which do not appear on the current Advanced Placement list of figures of speech. Because we aim this workbook beyond an audience of AP* students, and because lovers of Latin literature always want to dig more deeply when they can, we call attention to some of these devices with the designation "figure of speech (non-AP)." These include juxtaposition, repetition for pathos or pathetic effect, meiosis, and rhetorical question. When students are asked to identify a figure of speech on the Advanced Placement Examination, though, as opposed to discussing Horace's technique in an essay, we believe they are best advised to select only those on the Advanced Placement list.

It is our hope that this workbook will facilitate and strengthen the reading of Horace in Latin for both high school and college students. Horace's Latin can be difficult at times, but with work and with practice we trust that reading it will be a rewarding experience as it has been for both of us.

In conclusion, we would like to acknowledge several individuals for their direct and indirect help with this project. LeaAnn Osburn, our editor, gave us the opportunity to write this workbook and offered help, advice, and encouragement at various stages of the writing process. The manuscript benefited from her careful reading and commenting as well as that of Donald Sprague, who joined the editorial

* AP is a registered trademark of the College Entrance Examination Board, which was not involved in the production of, and does not endorse, this product.

effort towards the end, and that of the two anonymous peer reviewers for Bolchazy-Carducci Publishers. To Panayotes Dakouras, David Murphy's colleague at The Nightingale-Bamford School, we owe thanks for his willingness to test in the classroom some of our workbook materials-in-progress, and to his Advanced Placement Latin Literature students and David Murphy's Advanced Placement Vergil students of 2004–05 we say thank you for providing us with feedback on various exercises. Without our Horace teachers we would probably not have written this book. Finally, our own students, past and present, by serving as an ideal audience as we wrote, helped to ground our work in the pedagogical framework for which it was meant.

David J. Murphy, Ph.D.,
The Nightingale-Bamford School

Ronnie Ancona, Ph.D.,
Hunter College and The Graduate Center (CUNY)

TEXT OF
SATIRE 1.9
WITH EXERCISES

SATIRE 1.9.1–37

Ibam forte via sacra, sicut meus est mos,
nescio quid meditans nugarum, totus in illis.
accurrit quidam notus mihi nomine tantum,
arreptaque manu: 'quid agis, dulcissime rerum?'
'suaviter, ut nunc est' inquam, 'et cupio omnia, quae vis.'   5
cum adsectaretur: 'numquid vis?' occupo, at ille
'noris nos' inquit, 'docti sumus.' hic ego: 'pluris
hoc' inquam 'mihi eris.' misere discedere quaerens
ire modo ocius, interdum consistere, in aurem
dicere nescio quid puero, cum sudor ad imos   10
manaret talos. 'o te, Bolane, cerebri
felicem' aiebam tacitus, cum quidlibet ille
garriret, vicos, urbem laudaret. ut illi
nil respondebam: 'misere cupis' inquit 'abire;
iam dudum video. sed nil agis; usque tenebo.   15
persequar hinc, quo nunc iter est tibi.' 'nil opus est te
circumagi: quendam volo visere non tibi notum;
trans Tiberim longe cubat is prope Caesaris hortos.'
'nil habeo, quod agam, et non sum piger: usque sequar te.'
demitto auriculas, ut iniquae mentis asellus,   20
cum gravius dorso subiit onus. incipit ille:
'si bene me novi, non Viscum pluris amicum,
non Varium facies: nam quis me scribere pluris
aut citius possit versus? quis membra movere
mollius? invideat quod et Hermogenes ego canto.'   25
interpellandi locus hic erat: 'est tibi mater,
cognati, quis te salvo est opus?' 'haud mihi quisquam;
omnis composui.' 'felices! nunc ego resto.
confice! namque instat fatum mihi triste, Sabella
quod puero cecinit divina mota anus urna: 30
hunc neque dira venena, nec hosticus auferet ensis,
nec laterum dolor aut tussis, nec tarda podagra:
garrulus hunc quando consumet cumque. loquaces,
si sapiat, vitet, simul atque adoleverit aetas.'
ventum erat ad Vestae, quarta iam parte diei   35
praeterita, et casu tum respondere vadato
debebat, quod ni fecisset, perdere litem.

Short Answer Questions

Line 1   What is the case and use of *via sacra?* _____

Line 2   What is the case and use of *nugarum?* _____

Line 3   What is the case and use of *nomine?* _____

Line 4   What is the case and use of *manu?* _____

Line 5   What is the form of *vis?* _____

Line 7   What is the translation of *hic?* _____

Line 10   What is the case and use of *puero?* _____

Line 12   What is the case and use of *quidlibet?* _____

Line 14   What does *misere* modify? _____

Line 16   What is the translation of *quo?* _____

              What is the case and use of *tibi?* _____

Line 17   What form is *circumagi?* _____

              What is the case and use of *quendam?* _____

Line 18   What is the case and use of *is?* _____

              What is the case and use of *hortos?* _____

Line 19   What is a good, idiomatic translation of *nil habeo, quod agam?* _____

Line 20   What figures of speech are in this line? _____

              What is the case and use of *mentis?* _____

Line 21   What is a good, idiomatic translation of *gravius?* _____

              What is the case and use of *dorso?* _____

Lines 23–24   What figure of speech (non-AP) is in these lines? _____

Line 26   What part of speech is *interpellandi* and what other word in the sentence provides the cause for its grammatical case? _____

              What is the case and use of *tibi?* _____

Line 29   What is the case and use of *fatum?* _____

              What is the case and use of *Sabella?* _____

Line 31   To what does *hunc* refer? _____

              What is the case and use of *venena?* _____

              What two figures of speech are in this line? _____

Line 32   What is the case and use of *laterum*? _____

                 What figure of speech is in this line? _____

Line 33   What is the case and use of *loquaces*? _____

Line 34   What is the translation of *si sapiat, vitet,* and by what name do we classify this kind of conditional sentence? _____

                 What is the tense of *adoleverit*? _____

Line 35   What is the case and use of *diei*? _____

Line 36   What is the case and use of *casu*? _____

Line 37   What is the case and use of *quod*? _____

                 What is the best translation in its context of *ni fecisset*? _____

_____

Multiple Choice Questions *Suggested time: 15 minutes*

```
Ibam forte via sacra, sicut meus est mos,
nescio quid meditans nugarum, totus in illis.
accurrit quidam notus mihi nomine tantum,
arreptaque manu: 'quid agis, dulcissime rerum?'
'suaviter, ut nunc est' inquam, 'et cupio omnia, quae vis.'          5
cum adsectaretur: 'numquid vis?' occupo, at ille
'noris nos' inquit, 'docti sumus.' hic ego: 'pluris
hoc' inquam 'mihi eris.' misere discedere quaerens
ire modo ocius, interdum consistere, in aurem
dicere nescio quid puero, cum sudor ad imos                          10
manaret talos. 'o te, Bolane, cerebri
felicem' aiebam tacitus, cum quidlibet ille
garriret, vicos, urbem laudaret. ut illi
nil respondebam: 'misere cupis' inquit 'abire;
```

1.   From lines 1–2, we learn that Horace was

    a. going to make sacrifices   b. taking an unaccustomed route

    c. lost in thought   d. setting out bravely

2.   The character mentioned in line 3 was

    a. a friend of Horace   b. a recent acquaintance of Horace

    c. a professional associate of Horace   d. a man Horace knew only by name

3.   The behavior of the character described in lines 3–4 is best described as

    a. considerate   b. hostile

    c. presumptuous   d. tentative

4. From lines 5–6, we may infer that Horace hopes that the man will

   a. go away
   b. want all the same things he wants
   c. follow him
   d. speak pleasantly

5. In line 4, the best translation of *quid agis* is

   a. how are you doing
   b. which are you doing
   c. what are you driving
   d. why are you doing

6. The words *hic ego*: '*pluris hoc . . . .mihi eris*' (lines 7–8) are translated

   a. I say this: you will be more to me than this
   b. I am this one: you will be full with this for me
   c. here I say: you will be worth more to me because of this
   d. I say at this point: you will be more valuable to me than to him

7. Horace's mood in lines 8–11 is best described as

   a. desperate
   b. frightened
   c. sad
   d. angry

8. In line 8, *misere* modifies

   a. *discedere* (line 8)
   b. *quaerens* (line 8)
   c. *ire* (line 9)
   d. *consistere* (line 9)

9. The case of *puero* (line 10) is determined by

   a. *quid* (line 10)
   b. *nescio* (line 10)
   c. *dicere* (line 10)
   d. *aurem* (line 9)

10. The person described as *puero* (line 10) is Horace's

    a. slave
    b. son
    c. young friend
    d. student

11. The metrical pattern of the first four feet of line 12 is

    a. dactyl-dactyl-dactyl-spondee
    b. spondee-spondee-dactyl-spondee
    c. dactyl-spondee-dactyl-spondee
    d. spondee-spondee-spondee-dactyl

12. A figure of speech found in line 13 is

    a. syncope
    b. hyperbole
    c. hysteron proteron
    d. asyndeton

13. The case and number of *illi* (line 13) are

    a. genitive singular
    b. dative singular
    c. nominative plural
    d. ablative singular

Translation *Suggested time: 10 minutes*

Translate the passage below as literally as possible.

>'si bene me novi, non Viscum pluris amicum,
>non Varium facies: nam quis me scribere pluris
>aut citius possit versus? quis membra movere
>mollius? invideat quod et Hermogenes ego canto.'
>interpellandi locus hic erat: 'est tibi mater . . . ?'

_____

_____

_____

_____

_____

_____

_____

_____

_____

_____

Short Analysis Questions *Suggested time: 10 minutes*

>interpellandi locus hic erat: 'est tibi mater,
>cognati, quis te salvo est opus?' 'haud mihi quisquam;
>omnis composui.' 'felices! nunc ego resto.
>confice! namque instat fatum mihi triste, Sabella
>quod puero cecinit divina mota anus urna: 5
>hunc neque dira venena, nec hosticus auferet ensis,
>nec laterum dolor aut tussis, nec tarda podagra:
>garrulus hunc quando consumet cumque. loquaces,
>si sapiat, vitet, simul atque adoleverit aetas.'

1.   a.   Where are the family members of the person talking to the speaker?

_____

      b.   What does the speaker hope to accomplish by bringing up this person's family?

_____

2.   What does the speaker reveal about his feelings when he says *"felices! nunc ego resto"* (line 3)? Write out and translate a Latin word or phrase and explain how it supports your answer.

_____

_____

3.   According to lines 4–9, a prophecy was made about the speaker.

   a.   Who made this prophecy? _____

   b.   When was this prophecy made? _____

   c.   What does the prophecy foretell will be the cause of the speaker's death?

   _____

   _____

4.   Copy and scan line 5 (*quod . . . urna*).

_____

Essay *Suggested time: 20 minutes*

accurrit quidam notus mihi nomine tantum,
arreptaque manu: 'quid agis, dulcissime rerum?'
'suaviter, ut nunc est' inquam, 'et cupio omnia, quae vis.'   5
cum adsectaretur: 'numquid vis?' occupo, at ille
'noris nos' inquit, 'docti sumus.' hic ego: 'pluris
hoc' inquam 'mihi eris.' misere discedere quaerens
ire modo ocius, interdum consistere, in aurem
dicere nescio quid puero, cum sudor ad imos   10
manaret talos. 'o te, Bolane, cerebri
felicem' aiebam tacitus, cum quidlibet ille
garriret, vicos, urbem laudaret. ut illi
nil respondebam: 'misere cupis' inquit 'abire;
iam dudum video. sed nil agis; usque tenebo.   15
persequar hinc, quo nunc iter est tibi.' 'nil opus est te
circumagi: quendam volo visere non tibi notum;
trans Tiberim longe cubat is prope Caesaris hortos.'
'nil habeo, quod agam, et non sum piger: usque sequar te.'
demitto auriculas, ut iniquae mentis asellus,   20
cum gravius dorso subiit onus.

One of the elements that contributes to the humor of this satire is the conflict within the speaker between the desire to be polite to the person who addresses him and the desire to get rid of him. In a **brief,** well-organized essay, show how Horace represents this conflict.

Support your assertions with references drawn from **throughout** the passage. All Latin words must be copied or their line numbers provided, AND they must be translated or paraphrased closely enough so that it is clear you understand the Latin. It is your responsibility to convince your reader that you are basing your conclusions on the Latin text and not merely on a general recollection of the passage. Direct your answer to the question; do not merely summarize the passage. Please write your essay on a separate piece of paper.

Scansion

Scan the following lines and name the meter.

Ibam forte via sacra, sicut meus est mos,

nescio quid meditans nugarum, totus in illis.

accurrit quidam notus mihi nomine tantum,

arreptaque manu: 'quid agis, dulcissime rerum?'

'suaviter , ut nunc est' inquam, 'et cupio omnia, quae vis.'   5

cum adsectaretur: 'numquid vis?' occupo, at ille

SATIRE 1.9.38–78

'si me amas' inquit, 'paulum hic ades.' 'inteream, si
aut valeo stare aut novi civilia iura,
et propero, quo scis.' 'dubius sum, quid faciam' inquit,   40
'tene relinquam, an rem.' 'me, sodes.' 'non faciam' ille,
et praecedere coepit. ego, ut contendere durum
cum victore, sequor. 'Maecenas quomodo tecum?'
hinc repetit, 'paucorum hominum et mentis bene sanae;
nemo dexterius fortuna est usus. haberes   45
magnum adiutorem, posset qui ferre secundas,
hunc hominem velles si tradere. dispeream, ni
summosses omnis.' 'non isto vivimus illic,
quo tu rere, modo. domus hac nec purior ulla est,
nec magis his aliena malis. nil mi officit, inquam,   50
ditior hic aut est quia doctior: est locus uni
cuique suus.' 'magnum narras, vix credibile.' 'atqui
sic habet.' 'accendis, quare cupiam magis illi
proxumus esse.' 'velis tantummodo: quae tua virtus,
expugnabis, et est, qui vinci possit, eoque   55
difficilis aditus primos habet.' 'haud mihi dero:
muneribus servos corrumpam; non, hodie si
exclusus fuero, desistam; tempora quaeram,
occurram in triviis, deducam. nil sine magno
vita labore dedit mortalibus.' haec dum agit, ecce   60
Fuscus Aristius occurrit, mihi carus et illum
qui pulchre nosset. consistimus. 'unde venis?' et
'quo tendis?' rogat et respondet. vellere coepi
et pressare manu lentissima brachia, nutans,
distorquens oculos, ut me eriperet. male salsus   65
ridens dissimulare, meum iecur urere bilis:
'certe nescio quid secreto velle loqui te
aiebas mecum.' 'memini bene, sed meliore
tempore dicam: hodie tricesima sabbata. vin tu
curtis Iudaeis oppedere?' 'nulla mihi' inquam   70
'religio est.' 'at mi! sum paulo infirmior, unus
multorum. ignosces; alias loquar.' huncine solem
tam nigrum surrexe mihi! fugit inprobus ac me
sub cultro linquit. casu venit obvius illi
adversarius et 'quo tu, turpissime?' magna   75
inclamat voce, et 'licet antestari?' ego vero
oppono auriculam. rapit in ius: clamor utrimque,
undique concursus. sic me servavit Apollo.

Short Answer Questions

Line 39   What is the case and use of *civilia iura?* _____

Line 40   What part of speech is *quo?* _____

Line 41   What is the tense and mood of *faciam?* _____

               What figure of speech is in this line? _____

Line 42   What figure of speech is in this line? _____

               Translate *ut.* _____

Line 45   Translate *dexterus.* _____

Line 46   What two figures of speech (one non-AP) are in this line? _____

               _____

Line 48   What word does *isto* modify? _____

               To what does *illic* refer? _____

Line 49   What is the case and use of *hac?* _____

Line 50   What does *magis* modify? _____

Line 51   To what does *hic* refer? _____

               What is the case and use of *uni?* _____

Line 52   What is the case and use of *magnum?* _____

Line 53   What is the tense and mood of *cupiam?* _____

               What is the case and use of *illi?* _____

Line 54   What is the tense and mood of *velis?* _____

Line 55   What is the object of *expugnabis?* _____

               What figure of speech is in this line? _____

Line 56   What is the case and use of *aditus?* _____

Line 57   What is the case and use of *muneribus?* _____

Line 58   To what does *tempora* refer? _____

Line 59   What is the case and use of *nil?* _____

Line 60   What is the case and use of *mortalibus?* _____

Line 61   To what does *illum* refer? _____

Line 64   What is the case and use of *manu?* _____

               What does *lentissima* modify? _____

Line 65   What type of clause does *ut* introduce? _____

What does *salsus* modify? _____

Line 66   What two figures of speech are in this line? _____

Line 67   What is the case and use of *te?* _____

Line 69   What is the case and use of *tempore?* _____

Line 70   What is the case and use of *mihi?* _____

Line 71   What is the case and use of *paulo?* _____

Line 73   What is the case and use of *mihi?* _____

What does *inprobus* modify? _____

Line 74   What figure of speech is in this line? _____

To what does *illi* refer? _____

Line 77   What is the direct object of *rapit?* _____

Multiple Choice Questions *Suggested time: 15 minutes*

'si me amas' inquit, 'paulum hic ades.' 'inteream, si
aut valeo stare aut novi civilia iura,
et propero, quo scis.' 'dubius sum, quid faciam' inquit,
'tene relinquam, an rem.' 'me, sodes.' 'non faciam' ille,
et praecedere coepit. ego, ut contendere durum   5
cum victore, sequor. 'Maecenas quomodo tecum?'
hinc repetit, 'paucorum hominum et mentis bene sanae;
nemo dexterius fortuna est usus. haberes
magnum adiutorem, posset qui ferre secundas,
hunc hominem velles si tradere. dispeream, ni   10
summosses omnis.'

1. In line 1, *inteream* appears in a clause that expresses
    a. purpose   b. condition
    c. deliberation   d. wish

2. In line 2, *novi* is translated
    a. of the new   b. I know
    c. I knew   d. the new ones

3. The case and number of *civilia* (line 2) are
    a. accusative plural   b. nominative plural
    c. nominative singular d. ablative singular

4. In line 3, *quo* is translated
    a. by which
    b. for whom
    c. to what place
    d. as

5. In lines 1–3, Horace does NOT say that he
    a. is in a hurry
    b. is bored with the conversation
    c. is not able to appear as an advocate
    d. has no legal knowledge

6. From lines 3–5, we learn that Horace's interlocutor is willing to
    a. abandon the conversation
    b. hold Horace to his word
    c. stop and consider what to do
    d. lose his case in court

7. The expression closest in meaning to *sodes* (line 4) is
    a. *comes*
    b. *si vis*
    c. *amice*
    d. *se audis*

8. A figure of speech that occurs in line 6 is
    a. ellipsis
    b. chiasmus
    c. hyperbole
    d. apostrophe

9. The case of *mentis* (line 7) is determined by
    a. *paucorum* (line 7)
    b. *bene* (line 7)
    c. an understood *homo*
    d. *hominum* (line 7)

10. The metrical pattern of the first four feet of line 7 is
    a. dactyl-spondee-dactyl-spondee
    b. dactyl-dactyl-dactyl-spondee
    c. spondee-spondee-dactyl-spondee
    d. dactyl-spondee-spondee-dactyl

11. In lines 8–10, Horace's interlocutor promises to
    a. listen enthusiastically
    b. be a help
    c. bring second-best things
    d. receive a mutual friend

12. In line 10, *hominem* refers to
    a. the poet
    b. Maecenas
    c. the slave
    d. the person speaking to Horace

13. In line 11, the case of *omnis* is
    a. nominative
    b. accusative
    c. genitive
    d. ablative

14. The tense and mood of *summosses* (line 11) are
    a. pluperfect subjunctive
    b. future indicative
    c. imperfect subjunctive
    d. present indicative

Translation *Suggested time: 10 minutes*

Translate the passage below as literally as possible.

> '. . . nil mi officit, inquam,
> ditior hic aut est quia doctior: est locus uni
> cuique suus.' 'magnum narras, vix credibile.' 'atqui
> sic habet.' 'accendis, quare cupiam magis illi
> proxumus esse.' 'velis tantummodo: quae tua virtus, 5
> expugnabis, et est, qui vinci possit, . . .

_____

_____

_____

_____

_____

_____

_____

_____

_____

_____

_____

_____

Short Analysis Questions *Suggested time: 10 minutes*

> . . . casu venit obvius illi
> adversarius et 'quo tu, turpissime?' magna
> inclamat voce, et 'licet antestari?' ego vero
> oppono auriculam. rapit in ius: clamor utrimque,
> undique concursus. sic me servavit Apollo. 5

1. In lines 1–2,

   a. who is the *adversarius?* _____

   b. to whom is he speaking? _____

    c.   why does he address this person as *turpissime?*

_____

_____

2.   In line 3, what does the *adversarius* want to happen?

_____

_____

3.   Copy and scan line 4 (*oppono . . . utrimque*) and name the meter.

_____

_____

4.   In line 4,

    a.   what action is meant by *oppono auriculam?*

_____

    b.   what is the legal significance of this action?

_____

_____

Essay *Suggested time: 20 minutes*

. . . haec dum agit, ecce	
Fuscus Aristius occurrit, mihi carus et illum	
qui pulchre nosset. consistimus. 'unde venis?' et	
'quo tendis?' rogat et respondet. vellere coepi	
et pressare manu lentissima brachia, nutans,	5
distorquens oculos, ut me eriperet. male salsus	
ridens dissimulare, meum iecur urere bilis:	
'certe nescio quid secreto velle loqui te	
aiebas mecum.' 'memini bene, sed meliore	
tempore dicam: hodie tricesima sabbata. vin tu	10
curtis Iudaeis oppedere?' 'nulla mihi' inquam	
'religio est.' 'at mi! sum paulo infirmior, unus	
multorum. ignosces; alias loquar.' huncine solem	
tam nigrum surrexe mihi! fugit inprobus ac me	
sub cultro linquit.	15

One of the elements that contribute to the humor of *Satire* 1.9 is Horace's representation of character. In a **brief**, well-organized essay, discuss the ways in which Horace creates an impression of the character of Aristius Fuscus, and show how this depiction of Fuscus' character contributes to the satire's humor.

Support your assertions with references drawn from **throughout** the passage. All Latin words must be copied or their line numbers provided, AND they must be translated or paraphrased closely enough so that it is clear you understand the Latin. It is your responsibility to convince your reader that you are basing your conclusions on the Latin text and not merely on a general recollection of the passage. Direct your answer to the question; do not merely summarize the passage. Please write your essay on a separate piece of paper.

Scansion

Scan the following lines and name the meter.

nemo dexterius fortuna est usus. haberes

magnum adiutorem, posset qui ferre secundas,

hunc hominem velles si tradere. dispeream, ni

summosses omnis.' 'non isto vivimus illic,

quo tu rere, modo. domus hac nec purior ulla est,   5

nec magis his aliena malis. nil mi officit, inquam,

TEXT OF
ODES
WITH EXERCISES

ODE 1.1

Maecenas atavis edite regibus,
o et praesidium et dulce decus meum:
sunt, quos curriculo pulverem Olympicum
collegisse iuvat metaque fervidis
evitata rotis palmaque nobilis   5
terrarum dominos evehit ad deos;
hunc, si mobilium turba Quiritium
certat tergeminis tollere honoribus,
illum, si proprio condidit horreo,
quicquid de Libycis verritur areis.   10
gaudentem patrios findere sarculo
agros Attalicis condicionibus
numquam demoveas, ut trabe Cypria
Myrtoum pavidus nauta secet mare;
luctantem Icariis fluctibus Africum   15
mercator metuens otium et oppidi
laudat rura sui, mox reficit rates
quassas indocilis pauperiem pati.
est, qui nec veteris pocula Massici
nec partem solido demere de die   20
spernit, nunc viridi membra sub arbuto
stratus, nunc ad aquae lene caput sacrae;
multos castra iuvant et lituo tubae
permixtus sonitus bellaque matribus
detestata; manet sub Iove frigido   25
venator tenerae coniugis inmemor,
seu visa est catulis cerva fidelibus,
seu rupit teretes Marsus aper plagas.
me doctarum hederae praemia frontium
dis miscent superis, me gelidum nemus   30
Nympharumque leves cum Satyris chori
secernunt populo, si neque tibias
Euterpe cohibet, nec Polyhymnia
Lesboum refugit tendere barbiton.
quodsi me lyricis vatibus inseres,   35
sublimi feriam sidera vertice.

Short Answer Questions

Line 1   What figure of speech is in this line? _____

             What is the case and use of *atavis?* _____

             What is the case and use of *edite?* _____

             What is the case and use of *regibus?* _____

Line 2   What is the case and use of *praesidium?* _____

             What figure of speech is in this line? _____

Line 3   What is the case and use of *curriculo?* _____

Line 4   What is the form of *collegisse?*_____

             What is the case and use of *meta?* _____

Lines 4–5   What figure of speech is present in these lines? _____

Lines 5–6   What three figures of speech are in these lines? _____

Line 6   What is the case and use of *terrarum?* _____

Line 8   What figure of speech is in this line? _____

             What is the case and use of *honoribus?* _____

Lines 9–10   What is the direct object of *condidit?* _____

Line 11   What is the function of *gaudentem?* _____

             On what other word in the sentence does *findere* depend? _____

             What is the case and use of *sarculo?* _____

Line 12   What two figures of speech are in this line? _____

             What is the case and use of *condicionibus?* _____

Line 13   What is the case and use of *trabe?* _____

Line 14   What figure of speech is in this line? _____

Line 15   What two figures of speech are in this line? _____

Line 16   What is the direct object of *metuens?*_____

             What is the case and use of *oppidi?* _____

Line 17   What are the direct objects of *laudat?* _____

Line 18   What is the case and use of *indocilis?* _____

             What is the case and use of *pauperiem?*_____

Lines 20–21   What figure of speech is in these lines? _____

On what other word in the sentence does *demere* depend? _____

Lines 21–22   What two figures of speech are in these lines? _____

What is the case and use of *membra?* _____

Line 22   What does *stratus* modify? _____

What figure of speech is in this line? _____

Line 23   What is the case and use of *multos?* _____

What are the subjects of *iuvant?* _____

What is the case and use of *tubae?* _____

Lines 24–25   What figure of speech is in these lines? _____

Line 26   What figure of speech is present in this line? _____

What is the case and use of *coniugis?* _____

Line 27   What is the case and use of *catulis?* _____

Line 28   What figure of speech is in this line? _____

Line 29   What is the case and use of *me?* _____

What is the case and use of *hederae?* _____

What is the case and use of *praemia?* _____

What is the case and use of *frontium?* _____

What two figures of speech are in this line? _____

Line 30   What two figures of speech are in this line? _____

Line 32   What are the subjects of *secernunt?* _____

What is the case and use of *populo?* _____

Line 35   What is the case and use of *vatibus?* _____

Lines 35–36   What tense are *inseres* and *feriam?* Name the type of conditional sentence that is in these lines. _____

Line 36   What does *sublimi* modify? _____

What two figures of speech are in this line? _____

What is the case and use of *vertice?* _____

Multiple Choice Questions *Suggested time: 15 minutes*

gaudentem patrios findere sarculo
agros Attalicis condicionibus
numquam demoveas, ut trabe Cypria
Myrtoum pavidus nauta secet mare;
luctantem Icariis fluctibus Africum   5
mercator metuens otium et oppidi
laudat rura sui, mox reficit rates
quassas indocilis pauperiem pati.
est, qui nec veteris pocula Massici
nec partem solido demere de die   10
spernit, nunc viridi membra sub arbuto
stratus, nunc ad aquae lene caput sacrae;

1. In line 1, *gaudentem* describes a person who rejoices because he
   a. found his father's fields
   b. was paid a fortune
   c. becomes a sailor
   d. farms his native soil

2. The case of *condicionibus* (line 2) is determined by
   a. *numquam* (line 3)
   b. *Attalicis* (line 2)
   c. *findere* (line 1)
   d. *demoveas* (line 3)

3. In line 3, *demoveas* is translated
   a. you move away
   b. you would move away
   c. in order that you move away
   d. so that you may move away

4. A figure of speech contained in line 3 is
   a. synecdoche
   b. hyperbole
   c. personification
   d. transferred epithet

5. The words *luctantem . . . metuens* (lines 5–6) are translated
   a. the merchant, fearing the African wind wrestling with the Icarian waves
   b. with the Icarian winds flowing, the merchant fearing the struggling African wind
   c. amidst the Icarian waves, the merchant fearing the African wind wrestling
   d. the African wind contends with the Icarian waves as the merchant fears

6. From lines 7–8, we learn that the merchant
   a. praises commerce
   b. is poor
   c. rebuilds ships
   d. prefers the countryside to the sea

7. The case and number of *indocilis* (line 8) are

   a. ablative plural

   b. nominative singular

   c. genitive singular

   d. accusative plural

8. The form *pati* (line 8) is

   a. perfect participle

   b. perfect indicative

   c. present infinitive

   d. present imperative

9. In line 9, *veteris* modifies

   a. *qui* (line 9)

   b. the subject of *est* (line 9)

   c. the subject of *spernit* (line 11)

   d. *Massici* (line 9)

10. The person described in lines 9–12 (*est . . . sacrae*)

    a. takes time out from business

    b. despises drinking

    c. steals metal

    d. works in his garden

11. The case of *membra* (line 11) is determined by

    a. *arbuto* (line 11)

    b. *viridi* (line 11)

    c. *stratus* (line 12)

    d. *sub* (line 11)

12. In line 12, *caput* refers to a

    a. person's life

    b. source

    c. body part

    d. chief

13. A description of a person who devotes time to relaxation is

    a. *luctantem Icariis fluctibus Africum mercator metuens* (lines 5–6)

    b. *nec partem solido demere de die spernit* (lines 10–11)

    c. *pavidus nauta secet mare* (line 4)

    d. *mox reficit rates quassas* (lines 7–8)

Translation *Suggested time: 15 minutes*

Translate the passage below as literally as possible.

> multos castra iuvant et lituo tubae
> permixtus sonitus bellaque matribus
> detestata; manet sub Iove frigido
> venator tenerae coniugis inmemor,
> seu visa est catulis cerva fidelibus,
> seu rupit teretes Marsus aper plagas.
> me doctarum hederae praemia frontium
> dis miscent superis, . . .

5

_____

_____

_____

_____

_____

_____

_____

_____

_____

Short Analysis Questions *Suggested time: 10 minutes*

sunt, quos curriculo pulverem Olympicum
collegisse iuvat metaque fervidis
evitata rotis palmaque nobilis
terrarum dominos evehit ad deos;
hunc, si mobilium turba Quiritium   5
certat tergeminis tollere honoribus,
illum, si proprio condidit horreo,
quicquid de Libycis verritur areis.

1. What is the achievement of the people who are described in lines 1–4? Cite and translate or paraphrase closely two Latin words or phrases that support your answer.

    _____

    _____

    _____

2. Identify a figure of speech contained in lines 2–3 and write out the Latin words that illustrate it.

    _____

3. In lines 5–6,

    a. what is the *turba Quiritium?* _____

    b. what does it do that pleases the person referred to by the word *hunc* (line 5)?

    _____

4.   To what does *quicquid* in line 8 refer? Cite and translate or paraphrase closely the Latin words that support your answer.

_____

_____

_____

Essay *Suggested time: 20 minutes*

me doctarum hederae praemia frontium
dis miscent superis, me gelidum nemus
Nympharumque leves cum Satyris chori
secernunt populo, si neque tibias
Euterpe cohibet, nec Polyhymnia   5
Lesboum refugit tendere barbiton.
quodsi me lyricis vatibus inseres,
sublimi feriam sidera vertice.

In the passage above, Horace suggests that his poetic gifts win him special status. In a short, well-organized essay, explain what this status is and show how the poet expresses his claims to deserve it.

Support your assertions with references to the Latin text **throughout** the passage above. All Latin words must be copied or their line numbers provided, AND they must be translated or paraphrased closely enough so that it is clear you understand the Latin. It is your responsibility to convince the reader that you are basing your conclusions on the Latin text and not merely on a general recollection of the passage. Direct your answer to the question; do not merely summarize the passage. Please write your essay on a separate piece of paper.

Scansion

Scan the following lines and name the meter.

gaudentem patrios findere sarculo

agros Attalicis condicionibus

numquam demoveas, ut trabe Cypria

Myrtoum pavidus nauta secet mare;

luctantem Icariis fluctibus Africum   5

mercator metuens otium et oppidi

laudat rura sui, mox reficit rates

quassas indocilis pauperiem pati.

ODE 1.5

Quis multa gracilis te puer in rosa
perfusus liquidis urget odoribus
   grato, Pyrrha, sub antro?
     cui flavam religas comam

simplex munditiis? heu quotiens fidem   5
mutatosque deos flebit et aspera
   nigris aequora ventis
     emirabitur insolens,

qui nunc te fruitur credulus aurea,
qui semper vacuam, semper amabilem   10
   sperat, nescius aurae
     fallacis. miseri, quibus

intemptata nites. me tabula sacer
votiva paries indicat uvida
   suspendisse potenti   15
     vestimenta maris deo.

Short Answer Questions

Line 1   What figure of speech is in this line? _____

                What is the case and use of *te?*_____

Line 4   What is the case and use of *cui?*_____

                What is the subject and translation of *religas?* _____

Line 5   What is the case and use of *munditiis?* _____

Line 7   What is the case and use of *ventis?* _____

Line 8   What is the subject and translation of *emirabitur?*_____

Line 9   What is the case and use of *te?*_____

Line10   What two figures of speech are in this line? _____

                What is the translation of *vacuam* and what does it modify? _____

Line 11   What is the case and use of *aurae?*_____

Line 12   What is the antecedent, case, and use of *quibus?* _____

_____

Line13   What is the translation of *intemptata?* What does it modify?_____

_____

What figure of speech is in this line? _____

What is the case and use of *me?* _____

What is the case and use of *tabula?* _____

What is the case and use of *sacer?* _____

Line 14   What is the subject of *indicat?*_____

Lines 13–14   What figure of speech is in these lines? _____

Line 15   Why must *suspendisse* appear in the infinitive form? _____

Line 16   What is the case and use of *deo?* _____

Multiple Choice Questions *Suggested time: 12 minutes*

Quis multa gracilis te puer in rosa
perfusus liquidis urget odoribus
    grato, Pyrrha, sub antro?
      cui flavam religas comam

simplex munditiis? heu quotiens fidem   5
mutatosque deos flebit et aspera
    nigris aequora ventis
      emirabitur insolens,

qui nunc te fruitur credulus aurea,
qui semper vacuam, semper amabilem   10
    sperat, nescius aurae
      fallacis. miseri, quibus

intemptata nites. me tabula sacer
votiva paries indicat uvida
    suspendisse potenti   15
      vestimenta maris deo.

1.   In line 1, *multa gracilis . . . puer in rosa* is translated

    a. many slender boys in the roses   b. boy among many graceful roses

    c. slender boy in a large rose   d. slender boy among many a rose

2. From lines 1–3, we learn that the boy
   a. is urging Pyrrha to accept perfume
   b. is mixing scents with liquids
   c. has put much perfume on himself
   d. is pouring perfume on Pyrrha

3. The subject of *emirabitur* (line 8) is
   a. the boy
   b. Pyrrha
   c. the sea
   d. the god

4. The case of *te* (line 9) is determined by
   a. *fruitur* (line 9)
   b. *aurea* (line 9)
   c. *credulus* (line 9)
   d. *sperat* (line 11)

5. In its context, *vacuam* (line 10) implies
   a. empty-headed
   b. not stylish
   c. with few possessions
   d. available

6. A figure of speech that appears in line 12 is
   a. poetic plural
   b. elipsis
   c. transferred epithet
   d. simile

7. In line 12, *miseri* refers to
   a. Pyrrha's past lovers
   b. those who have yielded to temptation
   c. men whose advances fail to tempt Pyrrha
   d. those who are attracted to Pyrrha without experience of her

8. In line 14, *uvida* modifies
   a. *tabula* (line 13)
   b. *votiva* (line 14)
   c. *paries* (line 14)
   d. *vestimenta* (line 16)

9. The subject of *suspendisse* (line 15) is
   a. *me* (line 13)
   b. *paries* (line 13)
   c. *vestimenta* (line 16)
   d. *deo* (line 16)

10. What is **not** implied in lines 13–16?
   a. the speaker had an inscription put up
   b. the speaker dedicated his clothes in a temple
   c. the speaker's clothes are dripping
   d. Neptune saved the speaker

Translation *Suggested time: 10 minutes*

Translate the passage below as literally as possible.

> qui nunc te fruitur credulus aurea,
> qui semper vacuam, semper amabilem
> > sperat, nescius aurae
> > > fallacis. miseri, quibus
>
> intemptata nites. me tabula sacer   5
> votiva paries indicat uvida
> > suspendisse potenti
> > > vestimenta maris deo.

_____

_____

_____

_____

_____

_____

_____

_____

_____

_____

Short Analysis Questions *Suggested time: 10 minutes.*

simplex munditiis? heu quotiens fidem
mutatosque deos flebit et aspera
   nigris aequora ventis
     emirabitur insolens,

qui nunc te fruitur credulus aurea,   5
qui semper vacuam, semper amabilem
   sperat, nescius aurae
     fallacis. miseri, quibus

1. To whom does *simplex munditiis* refer in line 1? Translate the phrase and show how it contributes to the poet's characterization of this person.

   _____

   _____

   _____

2. What is the effect of the contrast between future and present time in lines 1–7? To support your answer, write out and translate two Latin words or phrases, one to show future and one to show present.

   _____

   _____

   _____

3. Name a figure of speech that appears in lines 2–3 and write out the Latin that illustrates it.

   _____

Essay *Suggested time: 20 minutes.*

Quis multa gracilis te puer in rosa
perfusus liquidis urget odoribus
   grato, Pyrrha, sub antro?
     cui flavam religas comam

simplex munditiis? heu quotiens fidem   5
mutatosque deos flebit et aspera
   nigris aequora ventis
     emirabitur insolens,

    qui nunc te fruitur credulus aurea,
    qui semper vacuam, semper amabilem   10
        sperat, nescius aurae
            fallacis. miseri, quibus

    intemptata nites. me tabula sacer
    votiva paries indicat uvida
        suspendisse potenti   15
            vestimenta maris deo.

Imagery of weather and seafaring are major elements of *Ode* 1.5. In a **short** essay, discuss how the speaker uses this imagery to talk about Pyrrha's treatment of men and about the men's reactions to her treatment of them.

Support your assertions with references to the Latin text. All Latin words must be copied or their line numbers provided, AND they must be translated or paraphrased closely enough so that it is clear you understand the Latin. It is your responsibility to convince your reader that you are basing your conclusions on the Latin text and not merely on your recollection of the passage. Direct your answer to the question; do not merely summarize the passage. Please write your essay on a separate piece of paper.

Scansion

Scan the following lines and name the meter.

Quis multa gracilis te puer in rosa

perfusus liquidis urget odoribus

    grato, Pyrrha, sub antro?

      cui flavam religas comam

simplex munditiis? heu quotiens fidem   **5**

mutatosque deos flebit et aspera

    nigris aequora ventis

      emirabitur insolens,

ODE 1.9

Vides, ut alta stet nive candidum
Soracte, nec iam sustineant onus
   silvae laborantes, geluque
     flumina constiterint acuto?

dissolve frigus ligna super foco   5
large reponens atque benignius
   deprome quadrimum Sabina,
     o Thaliarche, merum diota.

permitte divis cetera, qui simul
stravere ventos aequore fervido   10
   deproeliantis, nec cupressi
     nec veteres agitantur orni.

quid sit futurum cras, fuge quaerere, et
quem Fors dierum cumque dabit, lucro
   adpone, nec dulcis amores   15
     sperne puer neque tu choreas,

donec virenti canities abest
morosa. nunc et campus et areae
   lenesque sub noctem susurri
     composita repetantur hora,   20

nunc et latentis proditor intumo
gratus puellae risus ab angulo
   pignusque dereptum lacertis
     aut digito male pertinaci.

Short Answer Questions

Line 1   What is the translation of *ut?* _____

          Why is *stet* subjunctive? _____

Line 3   What is the case and use of *gelu?* _____

Line 4   What is the tense and mood of *constiterint?* _____

Line 5   What is the case and use of *ligna?* _____

Line 6   What is the part of speech and translation of *benignius?* _____

Line 9   What is the case and use of *divis?* _____

              What is the translation of *simul?* _____

Line 10   What form is *stravere?* _____

Lines 10–11   What two figures of speech are in this line? _____

Line 13   For what reason is *sit* subjunctive? _____

Line 14   What is the case and use of *lucro?* _____

Lines 17–18   What two figures of speech are in these lines? _____

Line 20   Why is *repetantur* subjunctive? _____

              What is the case and use of *hora?* _____

Line 21   What is the case and use of *proditor?* _____

Line 22   What is the case and use of *puellae?* _____

              What is the case and use of *risus?* _____

Line 23   What is the case and use of *pignus?* _____

              What is the case and use of *lacertis?* _____

Multiple Choice Questions *Suggested time: 15 minutes*

permitte divis cetera, qui simul
stravere ventos aequore fervido
    deproeliantis, nec cupressi
        nec veteres agitantur orni.

quid sit futurum cras, fuge quaerere, et   5
quem Fors dierum cumque dabit, lucro
    adpone, nec dulcis amores
        sperne puer neque tu choreas,

donec virenti canities abest
morosa. nunc et campus et areae   10
    lenesque sub noctem susurri
        composita repetantur hora,

nunc et latentis proditor intumo
gratus puellae risus ab angulo
    pignusque dereptum lacertis   15
        aut digito male pertinaci.

1. The case and number of *cetera* (line 1) are

    a. accusative plural   b. ablative singular
    c. nominative singular   d. nominative plural

2. The winds in lines 2–3 are described as

    a. seething   b. spreading
    c. sailing   d. fighting

3. The events that happen to the trees in lines 3–4 are cited as an example of how the gods

    a. destroy the proud   b. grant tranquillity
    c. create new life   d. contend in rivalry

4. One piece of advice found in lines 5–7 is to

    a. flee from tomorrow's dangers   b. seek knowledge of the future
    c. imitate the lucky   d. consider each day a gain

5. The case and number of *dulcis* (line 7) are

    a. accusative plural   b. ablative plural
    c. nominative singular   d. vocative singular

6. The case of *virenti* (line 9) is determined by
    a. *canities* (line 9)
    b. *morosa* (line 10)
    c. *donec* (line 9)
    d. *abest* (line 9)

7. The activity that the speaker has in mind in lines 10–12 is
    a. study
    b. love affairs
    c. attending the theatre
    d. voting

8. In line 12, *composita hora* is an ablative of
    a. cause
    b. manner
    c. specification
    d. time

9. Context makes clear that the *pignus* in line 15 is
    a. a sum of money
    b. a piece of jewelry
    c. a document
    d. a tree

10. The case of *digito* (line 16) is determined by
    a. *pignus* (line 15)
    b. *male* (line 16)
    c. *dereptum* (line 15)
    d. *lacertis* (line 15)

11. A figure of speech found in lines 13–14 is
    a. hyperbaton
    b. zeugma
    c. asyndeton
    d. hendiadys

Translation *Suggested time: 10 minutes.*

Translate the passage below as literally as possible.

> Vides, ut alta stet nive candidum
> Soracte, nec iam sustineant onus
>   silvae laborantes, geluque
>   flumina constiterint acuto?
>
> dissolve frigus ligna super foco   5
> large reponens atque benignius
>   deprome quadrimum Sabina,
>   o Thaliarche, merum diota.

_____

_____

_____

_____

_____

_____

_____

_____

_____

Short Analysis Questions *Suggested time: 10 minutes.*

> quid sit futurum cras, fuge quaerere, et
> quem Fors dierum cumque dabit, lucro
>   adpone, nec dulcis amores
>   sperne puer neque tu choreas,
>
> donec virenti canities abest   5
> morosa. nunc et campus et areae
>   lenesque sub noctem susurri
>   composita repetantur hora,

1.   In line 2,

    a.   translate *Fors.* _____

    b   identify the gift given by *Fors.* _____

2. To what does *canities* (line 5) refer literally and metaphorically?

   _____

3. What are two actions that the speaker proposes in lines 3–4? Write out and translate the Latin that refers to each action.

   _____

   _____

4. Name a figure of speech in line 2 and write out the Latin that illustrates it.

   _____

5. In what situation does the speaker envision the boy in lines 7–8? Cite two Latin words or phrases that support your answer.

   _____

   _____

   _____

Essay Question *Suggested time: 20 minutes.*

Vides, ut alta stet nive candidum
Soracte, nec iam sustineant onus
 silvae laborantes, geluque
  flumina constiterint acuto?

dissolve frigus ligna super foco   5
large reponens atque benignius
 deprome quadrimum Sabina,
  o Thaliarche, merum diota.

permitte divis cetera, qui simul
stravere ventos aequore fervido   10
 deproeliantis, nec cupressi
  nec veteres agitantur orni.

quid sit futurum cras, fuge quaerere, et
quem Fors dierum cumque dabit, lucro
 adpone, nec dulcis amores   15
  sperne puer neque tu choreas,

donec virenti canities abest
morosa. nunc et campus et areae
 lenesque sub noctem susurri
  composita repetantur hora,   20

nunc et latentis proditor intumo
gratus puellae risus ab angulo
pignusque dereptum lacertis
aut digito male pertinaci.

In a **short** essay, discuss how the imagery of the poem contributes to the advice about time and love given in the third and fourth stanzas.

Support your assertions with references to the Latin text. All Latin words must be copied or their line numbers provided, AND they must be translated or paraphrased closely enough so that it is clear you understand the Latin. It is your responsibility to convince your reader that you are basing your conclusions on the Latin text and not merely on your recollection of the passage. Direct your answer to the question; do not merely summarize the passage. Please write your essay on a separate piece of paper.

Scansion

Scan the following lines and name the meter.

permitte divis cetera, qui simul

stravere ventos aequore fervido

deproeliantis, nec cupressi

   nec veteres agitantur orni.

quid sit futurum cras, fuge quaerere, et   5

quem Fors dierum cumque dabit, lucro

   adpone, nec dulcis amores

      sperne puer neque tu choreas,

ODE 1.11

Tu ne quaesieris (scire nefas), quem mihi, quem tibi
finem di dederint, Leuconoe, nec Babylonios

temptaris numeros. ut melius, quidquid erit, pati!
seu pluris hiemes, seu tribuit Iuppiter ultimam,

quae nunc oppositis debilitat pumicibus mare   5
Tyrrhenum: sapias, vina liques et spatio brevi

spem longam reseces. dum loquimur, fugerit invida
aetas: carpe diem, quam minimum credula postero.

Short Answer Questions

Line 1   The verb *quaesieris* is an alternative of what verb form?_____

             What figure of speech is in this line? _____

             What part of speech is *quem*? _____

             What is the case and use of *mihi* and *tibi*? _____

Line 3   What is the case and use of *quidquid*? _____

             What form is *pati*? _____

Line 4   What is the case and use of *hiemes*? _____

Line 5   What is the antecedent, case, and use of *quae*? _____

             What is the case and use of *oppositis . . . pumicibus*? _____

Lines 5–6   What figure of speech is in these lines? _____

Line 6   What figure of speech is in this line? _____

Line 7   What two figures of speech are in this line? _____

Lines 7–8   What figure of speech is in these lines? _____

Line 8   What is the case and use of *postero*? _____

Multiple Choice Questions *Suggested time: 11 minutes.*

Tu ne quaesieris (scire nefas), quem mihi, quem tibi
finem di dederint, Leuconoe, nec Babylonios

temptaris numeros. ut melius, quidquid erit, pati!
seu pluris hiemes, seu tribuit Iuppiter ultimam,

quae nunc oppositis debilitat pumicibus mare   **5**
Tyrrhenum: sapias, vina liques et spatio brevi

spem longam reseces. dum loquimur, fugerit invida
aetas: carpe diem, quam minimum credula postero.

1. Lines 1–2 state that it is a crime to
   a. ignore the future
   c. tempt Babylonian numbers
   b. question the gods' will
   d. know what end the gods have given

2. The case of *mihi* (line 1) is determined by
   a. *quem* (line 1)
   c. *finem* (line 2)
   b. *di* (line 2)
   d. *dederint* (line 2)

3. *Pati* (line 3) is a form of
   a. pateo
   c. patior
   b. parco
   d. pasco

4. The case and number of *pluris* (line 4) are
   a. accusative plural
   c. nominative singular
   b. genitive singular
   d. dative plural

5. From lines 4–5, we learn that
   a. the sea weakens the pumice stones
   c. the rocks break the force of the sea
   b. Jupiter is worn out by the winter storm
   d. the sea opposes the god

6. In line 7, *fugerit* is literally translated as
   a. has fled
   c. flees
   b. will have fled
   d. will flee

7. In line 8, *quam minimum* is translated as
   a. which the smallest
   c. which least
   b. than the least
   d. as little as possible

8. In line 8, *credula* modifies

   a. the understood subject of *carpe* (line 8) b. *diem* (line 8)

   c. *aetas* (line 8) d. *quam* (line 8)

9. A figure of speech that appears in line 8 is

   a. hyperbole b. metaphor

   c. transferred epithet d. metonymy

Translation *Suggested time: 10 minutes.*

Translate the passage below as literally as possible.

> Tu ne quaesieris (scire nefas), quem mihi, quem tibi
> finem di dederint, Leuconoe, nec Babylonios
>
> temptaris numeros. ut melius, quidquid erit, pati!
> seu pluris hiemes, seu tribuit Iuppiter ultimam,
>
> quae nunc oppositis debilitat pumicibus mare   5
> Tyrrhenum: sapias, vina liques et spatio brevi

_____

_____

_____

_____

_____

_____

_____

_____

_____

Short Analysis Questions *Suggested time: 10 minutes.*

Tu ne quaesieris (scire nefas), quem mihi, quem tibi
finem di dederint, Leuconoe, nec Babylonios

temptaris numeros. ut melius, quidquid erit, pati!
seu pluris hiemes, seu tribuit Iuppiter ultimam,

quae nunc oppositis debilitat pumicibus mare   5
Tyrrhenum: sapias, vina liques et spatio brevi

spem longam reseces. dum loquimur, fugerit invida
aetas: carpe diem, quam minimum credula postero.

1. State two things Leuconoe is told not to do in lines 1–3. Cite and translate or accurately para-
    phrase the Latin that describes each action.

    _____

    _____

2. In line 4 the speaker contrasts two outcomes that Jupiter may assign.

    a. Name these outcomes. Cite and translate or accurately paraphrase the Latin that describes
        each outcome.

        _____

        _____

    b. What outcomes for the lives of Leuconoe and the speaker are represented by these alterna-
        tives?

        _____

        _____

3. Describe three things that the speaker tells Leuconoe to do in lines 6–7. Name the figure of
    speech in these lines.

    _____

    _____

    _____

    _____

4. What does the speaker say will happen while they speak (line 7)?

    _____

    _____

Essay *Suggested time: 20 minutes.*

Tu ne quaesieris (scire nefas), quem mihi, quem tibi
finem di dederint, Leuconoe, nec Babylonios

temptaris numeros. ut melius, quidquid erit, pati!
seu pluris hiemes, seu tribuit Iuppiter ultimam,

quae nunc oppositis debilitat pumicibus mare   5
Tyrrhenum: sapias, vina liques et spatio brevi

spem longam reseces. dum loquimur, fugerit invida
aetas: carpe diem, quam minimum credula postero.

This ode makes a contrast between things in life that the individual cannot control and things that
the individual **can** control. In a **short** essay, discuss how the speaker develops this contrast to help
him set forth advice about how to live. The quality of your essay will depend on the coherence of
your interpretation, your ability to account for the poem as a whole, and your use of the Latin to
support your interpretation.

Support your assertions with references to the Latin text **throughout** the poem. All Latin words must
be copied or their line numbers provided, AND they must be translated or paraphrased closely enough
so that it is clear you understand the Latin. It is your responsibility to convince your reader that you
are basing your conclusions on the Latin text and not merely on a general recollection of the passage.
Direct your answer to the question; do not merely summarize the passage. Please write your essay on
a separate piece of paper.

Scansion

Scan the following lines and name the meter.

quae nunc oppositis debilitat pumicibus mare

Tyrrhenum: sapias, vina liques et spatio brevi

spem longam reseces. dum loquimur, fugerit invida

aetas: carpe diem, quam minimum credula postero.

ODE 1.13

Cum tu, Lydia, Telephi
    cervicem roseam, cerea Telephi
laudas brachia, vae meum
    fervens difficili bile tumet iecur.

tunc nec mens mihi, nec color   5
    certa sede manet, umor et in genas
furtim labitur arguens,
    quam lentis penitus macerer ignibus.

uror, seu tibi candidos
    turparunt umeros inmodicae mero   10
rixae, sive puer furens
    inpressit memorem dente labris notam.

non, si me satis audias,
    speres perpetuum dulcia barbare
laedentem oscula, quae Venus   15
    quinta parte sui nectaris imbuit.

felices ter et amplius,
    quos inrupta tenet copula, nec malis
divolsus querimoniis
    suprema citius solvet amor die.   20

Short Answer Questions

Line 2   What is the case and use of *cervicem?* _____

Line 4   What is the case and use of *bile?* _____

Line 5   What is the case and use of *mihi?* _____

Line 6   What is the case and use of *sede?* _____

                What two figures of speech (one non-AP) are in these lines? _____

                _____

Line 7   What is the translation of *labitur?* _____

Line 8   What is the part of speech and translation of *quam?* _____

                For what reason is *macerer* subjunctive? _____

What is the case and use of *ignibus?* _____

Line 9   What figure of speech is in this line? _____

What is the case and use of *tibi?* _____

Line 10   What is the case and use of *mero?* _____

Line 12   What is the case and use of *dente?* _____

What is the case and use of *labris?*_____

Line 14   What is the tense and mood of *speres?* _____

What is the translation of *perpetuum,* and what does it modify? _____
_____

What is the part of speech and translation of *barbare?* _____

Line 15   What is the translation, case, and use of *laedentem?* _____

What is the case and use of *oscula?* _____

What is the antecedent of *quae?* _____

Line 16   What is the case and use of *parte?* _____

What is the case and use of *nectaris?* _____

Line 17   What figure of speech is in this line? _____

What is the part of speech and translation of *ter* and *amplius?* What do they modify?
_____

Line 18   What is the antecedent, case, and use of *quos?* _____

Line 19   What is the translation of *divolsus,* and what does it modify?_____
_____

What is the case and use of *querimoniis?*_____

Line 20   What is the translation and part of speech *citius?*_____

What tense of *solvet?* What is its direct object? _____

What is the case and use of *die?* _____

Multiple Choice Questions *Suggested time: 15 minutes.*

Cum tu, Lydia, Telephi
    cervicem roseam, cerea Telephi
laudas brachia, vae meum
    fervens difficili bile tumet iecur.

tunc nec mens mihi, nec color   5
    certa sede manet, umor et in genas
furtim labitur arguens,
    quam lentis penitus macerer ignibus.

uror, seu tibi candidos
    turparunt umeros inmodicae mero   10
rixae, sive puer furens
    inpressit memorem dente labris notam.

non, si me satis audias,
    speres perpetuum dulcia barbare
laedentem oscula, quae Venus   15
    quinta parte sui nectaris imbuit.

felices ter et amplius,
    quos inrupta tenet copula, nec malis
divolsus querimoniis
    suprema citius solvet amor die.   20

1. In line 1, *cum* is translated

    a. when   b. with

    c. since   d. although

2. In line 3, *meum* modifies

    a. *fervens*   b. *vae*

    c. *bile*   d. *iecur*

3. The case and number of *difficili* (line 4) are

    a. nominative plural   b. genitive singular

    c. ablative singular   d. dative singular

4. In lines 6–8, the speaker says that Lydia's praise of Telephus makes him

    a. stumble   b. speechless

    c. argue   d. weep

5. The case of *ignibus* (line 8) is determined by

   a. *penitus* (line 8)   b. *macerer* (line 8)

   c. *lentis* (line 8)   d. *quam* (line 8)

6. The best translation of *tibi . . . turparunt umeros . . . rixae* (lines 10–11) is

   a. for you they broke the back of the quarrel   b. quarrels disfigured your shoulders

   c. having quarreled, they bared their shoulders to you   d. your shoulders grew ugly in the quarrel

7. In lines 13–14, *non . . . speres* is translated

   a. you may not hope   b. you do not hope

   c. you should not hope   d. you would not hope

8. In line 15, *laedentem* modifies

   a. *me* (line 13)   b. the boy understood from line 11

   c. *barbare* (line 14)   d. an understood *te*

9. Lines 15–16 tell us that Venus

   a. sweetens Lydia's lips   b. bestows kisses

   c. flavors her own nectar   d. strikes Lydia's mouth

10. The antecedent of *quos* (line 18) is

   a. the speaker and the *puer*   b. the *puer* and Lydia

   c. an understood *ei*   d. *malis*

11. The case of *querimoniis* (line 19) is determined by

   a. *malis* (line 18)   b. *citius* (line 20)

   c. *solvet* (line 20)   d. *divolsus* (line 19)

12. The tense and mood of *solvet* (line 20) are

   a. present subjunctive   b. present indicative

   c. future indicative   d. imperfect subjunctive

13. In line 20, *suprema die* is the day of

   a. death   b. a religious festival

   c. the wedding   d. love's declaration

Translation *Suggested time: 15 minutes.*

Translate the passage below as literally as possible.

> uror, seu tibi candidos
>   turparunt umeros inmodicae mero
> rixae, sive puer furens
>   inpressit memorem dente labris notam.
>
> non, si me satis audias,   5
>   speres perpetuum dulcia barbare
> laedentem oscula, quae Venus
>   quinta parte sui nectaris imbuit.

_____

_____

_____

_____

_____

_____

_____

_____

_____

_____

Short Analysis Questions *Suggested time: 10 minutes.*

tunc nec mens mihi, nec color
    certa sede manet, umor et in genas
furtim labitur arguens,
    quam lentis penitus macerer ignibus.

uror, seu tibi candidos   5
    turparunt umeros inmodicae mero
rixae, sive puer furens
    inpressit memorem dente labris notam.

non, si me satis audias,
    speres perpetuum dulcia barbare   10
laedentem oscula, quae Venus
    quinta parte sui nectaris imbuit.

felices ter et amplius,
    quos inrupta tenet copula, nec malis
divolsus querimoniis   15
    suprema citius solvet amor die.

1.   a.   State **one** fact about **each** of these relationships: Lydia and Telephus; the speaker and Lydia.

          _____

          _____

     b.   As support for what you say, cite and translate or accurately paraphrase **one** Latin phrase for **each** fact (two Latin phrases in all).

          _____

          _____

2.   Identify a figure of speech found in lines 7–8 and write out the Latin words that illustrate it.

      _____

3.   In lines 9–11, what does the speaker advise Lydia not to do? Cite the Latin words that contain this advice.

      _____

      _____

4.   In the last stanza, how does the speaker describe those lovers who do not break up?

      _____

      _____

Essay *Suggested time: 20 minutes.*

Cum tu, Lydia, Telephi
    cervicem roseam, cerea Telephi
laudas brachia, vae meum
    fervens difficili bile tumet iecur.

tunc nec mens mihi, nec color   5
    certa sede manet, umor et in genas
furtim labitur arguens,
    quam lentis penitus macerer ignibus.

uror, seu tibi candidos
    turparunt umeros inmodicae mero   10
rixae, sive puer furens
    inpressit memorem dente labris notam.

non, si me satis audias,
    speres perpetuum dulcia barbare
laedentem oscula, quae Venus   15
    quinta parte sui nectaris imbuit.

In these stanzas, the speaker makes frequent reference to physical appearance or physical suffering as he tries to dissuade Lydia from her relationship with Telephus. In a **short** essay, discuss how the speaker uses references to physical appearance **and** to physical suffering to try to enhance the persuasive force of his speech.

Support your assertions with references to the Latin text **throughout** the passage. All Latin words must be copied or their line numbers provided, AND they must be translated or paraphrased closely enough so that it is clear you understand the Latin. It is your responsibility to convince your reader that you are basing your conclusions on the Latin text and not merely on a general recollection of the passage. Direct your answer to the question; do not merely summarize the passage. Please write your essay on a separate piece of paper.

Scansion

Scan the following lines and name the meter.

Cum tu, Lydia, Telephi

    cervicem roseam, cerea Telephi

laudas brachia, vae meum

    fervens difficili bile tumet iecur.

tunc nec mens mihi, nec color   5

    certa sede manet, umor et in genas

furtim labitur arguens,

    quam lentis penitus macerer ignibus.

ODE 1.22

Integer vitae scelerisque purus
non eget Mauris iaculis neque arcu,
nec venenatis gravida sagittis,
    Fusce, pharetra,

sive per Syrtis iter aestuosas   5
sive facturus per inhospitalem
Caucasum, vel quae loca fabulosus
    lambit Hydaspes.

namque me silva lupus in Sabina,
dum meam canto Lalagen et ultra   10
terminum curis vagor expeditis,
    fugit inermem,

quale portentum neque militaris
Daunias latis alit aesculetis,
nec Iubae tellus generat, leonum   15
    arida nutrix.

pone me, pigris ubi nulla campis
arbor aestiva recreatur aura,
quod latus mundi nebulae malusque
    Iuppiter urget,   20

pone sub curru nimium propinqui
solis in terra domibus negata:
dulce ridentem Lalagen amabo,
    dulce loquentem.

Short Answer Questions

Line 1   What figure of speech is in this line? _____

                 What is the case and use of *vitae?* _____

Line 2   What is the case and use of *iaculis* and *arcu?* _____

Line 4   What is the case and use of *Fusce?*_____

                 What is the case and use of *pharetra?* _____

Lines 5–8   What figure of speech is in these lines? _____

Line 5   What is the translation of *aestuosas,* and what does it modify?_____

_____

Line 6   What does *facturus* modify? _____

Line 7   What is the translation of *fabulosus,* and what does it modify?_____

_____

Line 9   What did the wolf do in this stanza? _____

What is the case and use of *me?* _____

Line 10   What is the case and use of *Lalagen?* _____

Line 11   Of what preposition is *terminum* the object? _____

What is the case and use of *curis . . . expeditis?*_____

Line 12   What is the translation of *inermem* and what does it modify?_____

_____

Line 13   To what in the preceding lines does the phrase *quale portentum* refer? _____

_____

Line 14   What is the case and use of *Daunias?* _____

What is the translation of *latis aesculetis?* _____

Line 15   What is the object of *generat?* _____

What is the case and use of *leonum?* _____

Line 16   What three figures of speech are in this line? _____

Line 17   What is the form of *pone?* _____

What does *nulla* modify?_____

What is the case and use of *campis?*_____

Line 18   What is the translation of *aestiva* and what does it modify? _____

_____

What is the case and use of *aura?* _____

Line 19   Of what verb is *nebulae* the subject?_____

Line 20   What figure of speech is in this line? _____

What is the translation of *urget,* and what is its object? _____

Line 21   What part of speech is *nimium,* and what does it modify?_____

_____

Line 22   What is the case and use of *solis?*_____

What is the case and use of *domibus?* _____

Lines 23–24   What part of speech is *dulce* and what does it modify in each instance?_____

_____

Lines 23–24   What figure of speech is in these lines? _____

Multiple Choice Questions *Suggested time: 15 minutes*

Integer vitae scelerisque purus
non eget Mauris iaculis neque arcu,
nec venenatis gravida sagittis,
        Fusce, pharetra,

sive per Syrtis iter aestuosas   5
sive facturus per inhospitalem
Caucasum, vel quae loca fabulosus
        lambit Hydaspes.

namque me silva lupus in Sabina,
dum meam canto Lalagen et ultra   10
terminum curis vagor expeditis,
        fugit inermem,

quale portentum neque militaris
Daunias latis alit aesculetis,
nec Iubae tellus generat, leonum   15
        arida nutrix.

1.   The case of *sceleris* (line 1) is determined by
      a. *eget* (line 2)   b. *vitae* (line 1)
      c. *integer* (line 1)   d. *purus* (line 1)

2.   A figure of speech contained in lines 2–4 is
      a. metaphor   b. tricolon crescens/crescendo
      c. hendiadys   d. chiasmus

3.   The case of *sagittis* (line 3) is determined by
      a. *venenatis* (line 3)   b. *eget* (line 2)
      c. *gravida* (line 3)   d. *pharetra* (line 4)

4.   The imagery of lines 1–4 evokes
      a. the Caucasus   b. India
      c. Africa   d. Italy

5. In line 5, *iter* is the object of

    a. *facturus* (line 6)   b. *per* (line 5)

    c. *lambit* (line 8)   d. *aestuosas* (line 5)

6. The case and number of *Syrtis* (line 5) are

    a. nominative singular   b. genitive singular

    c. ablative plural   d. accusative plural

7. The word *quae* (line 7) refers to

    a. *Hydaspes* (line 8)   b. *loca* (line 7)

    c. *Syrtis* (line 5)   d. *Caucasum* (line 7)

8. In lines 1–8, the poet claims that

    a. he will journey to foreign lands   b. Fuscus does not need weapons

    c. virtue is better protection than weapons   d. god safeguards the lover

9. The best translation of the words *dum . . . ultra terminum curis vagor expeditis* (lines 10–11) is

    a. while I wander beyond the boundary line and lay aside my cares   b. until I may wander beyond the boundary line, having laid aside my cares

    c. granted only that I lay aside my cares as I wander beyond the boundary line   d. while I was wandering beyond the boundary line, with cares laid aside

10. From lines 9–12, we learn that the poet was

    a. near his home   b. in southern Italy

    c. fleeing from a wolf   d. singing with his beloved

11. The translation of *fugit* (line 12) is

    a. flees   b. will flee

    c. fled   d. may flee

12. In line 13, *militaris* modifies

    a. *Daunias* (line 14)   b. *aesculetis* (line 14)

    c. *latis* (line 14)   d. *portentum* (line 13)

13. The best translation of *alit* (line 14) is

    a. salts   b. nourishes

    c. flies   d. gets down

14. In line 16, *nutrix* refers to

    a. *arida* (line 16)   b. *tellus* (line 15)

    c. *leonum* (line 15)   d. *Iubae* (line 15)

15. From lines 13–16, we can infer that the poet thinks that

    a. omens are to be despised

    b. oak forests have been brought to southern Italy

    c. lions are not found in the land of Iuba

    d. he saw an abnormal phenomenon

Translation *Suggested time: 15 minutes.*

Translate the passage below as literally as possible.

> Integer vitae scelerisque purus
> non eget Mauris iaculis neque arcu,
> nec venenatis gravida sagittis,
>   Fusce, pharetra,
>
> sive per Syrtis iter aestuosas   5
> sive facturus per inhospitalem
> Caucasum, vel quae loca fabulosus
>   lambit Hydaspes.

_____

_____

_____

_____

_____

_____

_____

_____

_____

Short Analysis Questions *Suggested time: 10 minutes.*

quale portentum neque militaris
Daunias latis alit aesculetis,
nec Iubae tellus generat, leonum
    arida nutrix.

pone me, pigris ubi nulla campis   5
arbor aestiva recreatur aura,
quod latus mundi nebulae malusque
    Iuppiter urget,

pone sub curru nimium propinqui
solis in terra domibus negata: 10
dulce ridentem Lalagen amabo,
    dulce loquentem.

1. Write out and scan lines 3–4 (*nec Iubae . . . nutrix*).

   _____

   _____

2. In lines 5–10, the poet imagines himself in two different landscapes.

   a. Describe **one** feature of **each** landscape.

   _____

   b. Cite and either translate or accurately paraphrase the Latin that supports your description of each feature.

   _____

   _____

3. In lines 11–12, the poet declares his feelings about Lalage.

   a. What are the poet's feelings about Lalage, and why does he feel this way?

   _____

   _____

   b. Refer specifically to the Latin that supports your answer.

   _____

   _____

Essay *Suggested time: 20 minutes*

Integer vitae scelerisque purus
non eget Mauris iaculis neque arcu,
nec venenatis gravida sagittis,
  Fusce, pharetra,

sive per Syrtis iter aestuosas   5
sive facturus per inhospitalem
Caucasum, vel quae loca fabulosus
  lambit Hydaspes.

namque me silva lupus in Sabina,
dum meam canto Lalagen et ultra   10
terminum curis vagor expeditis,
  fugit inermem,

quale portentum neque militaris
Daunias latis alit aesculetis,
nec Iubae tellus generat, leonum   15
  arida nutrix.

pone me, pigris ubi nulla campis
arbor aestiva recreatur aura,
quod latus mundi nebulae malusque
  Iuppiter urget,   20

pone sub curru nimium propinqui
solis in terra domibus negata:
dulce ridentem Lalagen amabo,
  dulce loquentem.

This ode contains many references to and descriptions of places. In a **short** essay, discuss how the poet uses place references to enhance his representation of himself in the role of lover.

Support your assertions with references to the Latin text **throughout** the poem. All Latin words must be copied or their line numbers provided, AND they must be translated or paraphrased closely enough so that it is clear you understand the Latin. It is your responsibility to convince your reader that you are basing your conclusions on the Latin text and not merely on a general recollection of the passage. Direct your answer to the question; do not merely summarize the passage. Please write your essay on a separate piece of paper.

Scansion

Scan the following lines and name the meter.

Integer vitae scelerisque purus

non eget Mauris iaculis neque arcu,

nec venenatis gravida sagittis,

    Fusce, pharetra,

sive per Syrtis iter aestuosas   5

sive facturus per inhospitalem

Caucasum, vel quae loca fabulosus

    lambit Hydaspes.

ODE 1.23

Vitas inuleo me similis, Chloe,
quaerenti pavidam montibus aviis
   matrem non sine vano
     aurarum et siluae metu.

nam seu mobilibus veris inhorruit   5
adventus foliis, seu virides rubum
   dimovere lacertae,
     et corde et genibus tremit.

atqui non ego te tigris ut aspera
Gaetulusve leo frangere persequor: 10
   tandem desine matrem
     tempestiva sequi viro.

Short Answer Questions

Line 1   What is the case and use of *me?* _____

               What figure of speech is in this line? _____

Line 2   What word does *quaerenti* modify? _____

               Translate *pavidam.* _____

               What word does *pavidam* modify? _____

               What is the case and use of *montibus aviis?* _____

Line 3   For what word does *matrem* serve as object? _____

               What word does *vano* modify? _____

Lines 2–3   What figure of speech is in these lines? _____

Line 4   What is the case and use of *aurarum et silvae?* _____

Line 5   What is the case and use of *veris?* _____

Line 6   What is the case and use of *adventus?* _____

               What is the case and use of *foliis?* _____

               What does *virides* modify? _____

               What is the case and use of *rubum?* _____

Line 7   The verb *dimovere* is an alternative of what verb? _____

Line 8   What is the case and use of *corde*? _____

Line 9   What three figures of speech (2 non-AP) are in this line? _____

               _____

               What is the case and use of *te*? _____

               What is the case and use of *tigris*? _____

Line 10   What is the case and use of *leo*? _____

               What verb form is *frangere*, and how is it used grammatically in its context? _____

               _____

Lines 9–10   What figure of speech is in these lines? _____

Line 11   What is the case and use of *matrem*? _____

Line 12   What is the translation of *tempestiva*? _____

               What word does *tempestiva* modify? _____

               What is the form of *sequi*? _____

               On what word does *sequi* depend? _____

               What is the case and use of *viro*? _____

Multiple Choice Questions *Suggested time: 14 minutes.*

Vitas inuleo me similis, Chloe,
quaerenti pavidam montibus aviis
    matrem non sine vano
      aurarum et siluae metu.

nam seu mobilibus veris inhorruit   5
adventus foliis, seu virides rubum
    dimovere lacertae,
      et corde et genibus tremit.

atqui non ego te tigris ut aspera
Gaetulusve leo frangere persequor: 10
    tandem desine matrem
      tempestiva sequi viro.

1.   In lines 1–4, the fawn is afraid of

    a. its mother   b. the speaker

    c. the breezes   d. Chloe

2. The case of *inuleo* (line 1) is determined by
   a. *vitas* (line 1)
   b. *me* (line 1)
   c. *quaerenti* (line 2)
   d. *similis* (line 1)

3. The person who is described as panicky in line 2 is
   a. the mother deer
   b. the fawn
   c. the speaker
   d. Chloe

4. A figure of speech contained in lines 2–3 is
   a. chiasmus
   b. synchysis
   c. zeugma
   d. hysteron proteron

5. The case and number of *veris* (line 5) are
   a. genitive singular
   b. ablative plural
   c. accusative plural
   d. nominative singular

6. The subject of *inhorruit* (line 5) is
   a. *inuleo* (line 1)
   b. *Chloe* (line 1)
   c. *veris* (line 5)
   d. *adventus* (line 6)

7. The form of the word *dimovere* (line 7) is
   a. present infinitive
   b. perfect indicative
   c. perfect participle
   d. present indicative

8. The meaning of *ut* in line 9 is
   a. that
   b. as
   c. how
   d. in order to

9. In line 9, *aspera* modifies
   a. *ego* (line 9)
   b. *te* (line 9)
   c. *tigris* (line 9)
   d. *leo* (line 10)

10. In lines 9–10, the speaker tells Chloe that
    a. she will not escape unharmed
    b. no tiger will chase after her
    c. she will avoid tigers and lions
    d. he will not harm her

11. The case of *viro* (line 12) is determined by
    a. *desine* (line 11)
    b. *sequi* (line 12)
    c. *tempestiva* (line 12)
    d. *tandem* (line 11)

12. In lines 11–12, the speaker tells Chloe that she
    a. should stop following a man
    b. is ready for a man
    c. should at last follow her mother
    d. must not be angry at her mother

Translation *Suggested time: 15 minutes.*

Translate as literally as possible.

> **Vitas inuleo me similis, Chloe,**
> **quaerenti pavidam montibus aviis**
> **matrem non sine vano**
> **aurarum et siluae metu.**
>
> **nam seu mobilibus veris inhorruit** 5
> **adventus foliis, seu virides rubum**
> **dimovere lacertae,**
> **et corde et genibus tremit.**

Short Analysis Questions *Suggested time: 10 minutes.*

Vitas inuleo me similis, Chloe,
quaerenti pavidam montibus aviis
   matrem non sine vano
     aurarum et siluae metu.

nam seu mobilibus veris inhorruit   **5**
adventus foliis, seu virides rubum
   dimovere lacertae,
     et corde et genibus tremit.

atqui non ego te tigris ut aspera
Gaetulusve leo frangere persequor: **10**
   tandem desine matrem
     tempestiva sequi viro.

1. Briefly describe the fawn's fear and its mother's fear in lines 1–4.

    _____

    _____

2. Name a figure of speech that occurs in lines 3–4, and write out the Latin word(s) that illustrate it.

    _____

3. In lines 5–8, the speaker gives two examples meant to show why he thinks that the fawn's emotions are groundless.

   a. Explain how each example, according to the speaker's argument, is an instance of groundless emotion.

       _____

       _____

   b. Cite and translate or paraphrase accurately the Latin that supports your case about each example.

       _____

       _____

4. What two reasons does the speaker offer Chloe in lines 9–12 for why she should favor him?

    _____

    _____

    _____

Essay *Suggested time: 20 minutes.*

Vitas inuleo me similis, Chloe,
quaerenti pavidam montibus aviis
   matrem non sine vano
     aurarum et siluae metu.

nam seu mobilibus veris inhorruit   5
adventus foliis, seu virides rubum
   dimovere lacertae,
     et corde et genibus tremit.

atqui non ego te tigris ut aspera
Gaetulusve leo frangere persequor: 10
   tandem desine matrem
     tempestiva sequi viro.

In this poem, Horace represents a speaker attempting a persuasive speech. Readers have differed in their views about the character of the speaker. In a **short,** well-organized essay, discuss how Horace creates an impression of the sort of person that the speaker is.

Support your assertions with references to the Latin text **throughout** the poem. All Latin words must be copied or their line numbers provided, AND they must be translated or paraphrased closely enough so that it is clear you understand the Latin. It is your responsibility to convince your reader that you are basing your conclusions on the Latin text and not merely on a general recollection of the passage. Direct your answer to the question; do not merely summarize the passage. Please write your essay on a separate piece of paper.

Scansion

Scan the following lines and name the meter.

nam seu mobilibus veris inhorruit

adventus foliis, seu virides rubum

dimovere lacertae,

et corde et genibus tremit.

atqui non ego te tigris ut aspera 5

Gaetulusve leo frangere persequor:

tandem desine matrem

tempestiva sequi viro.

ODE 1.24

Quis desiderio sit pudor aut modus
tam cari capitis? praecipe lugubris
cantus, Melpomene, cui liquidam pater
    vocem cum cithara dedit.

ergo Quintilium perpetuus sopor   5
urget? cui Pudor et Iustitiae soror,
incorrupta Fides nudaque Veritas
    quando ullum inveniet parem?

multis ille bonis flebilis occidit,
nulli flebilior, quam tibi, Vergili.   10
tu, frustra pius, heu, non ita creditum
    poscis Quintilium deos.

quid, si Threicio blandius Orpheo
auditam moderere arboribus fidem,
num vanae redeat sanguis imagini,   15
    quam virga semel horrida

non lenis precibus fata recludere
nigro compulerit Mercurius gregi?
durum, sed levius fit patientia,
    quicquid corrigere est nefas.   20

Short Answer Questions

Line 1   What is the translation of *quis*? _____

                    What is the case and use of *desiderio*? _____

Line 2   What figure of speech is in this line? _____

                    What is the case and use of *capitis*? _____

                    Who is to perform the action of the verb *praecipe*? _____

Lines 1–2   What figure of speech (non-AP) is in these lines?_____

Line 3   What is the case and use of *cantus*? _____

Line 6   What is the case and use of *cui*?_____

                    What is the function of *cui*? _____

Lines 5–6   What three figures of speech are in these lines? _____
               _____

Line 8   What is the function of *quando?* _____

               What is the function of *ullum?* _____

               What is the subject of *inveniet?* _____

               What is the case and use of *parem?* _____

Lines 5–8   What two figures of speech (2 non-AP) are in these lines? _____
               _____

Line 9   What is the case and use of *bonis?* _____

               What is its function? _____

               What does *flebilis* modify?_____

Line 10   What is the case and use of *nulli?* _____

               What is the case of *Vergili?* _____

Line 11   What does *creditum* modify? By whom and to whom was that person entrusted? ____
               _____

Line 12   What is the case and use of *Quintilium?* _____

               What is the case and use of *deos?*_____

Line 13   What is the form of *blandius?* _____

               What is the case and use of *Orpheo?* _____

Line 14   What is the case and use of *arboribus?*_____

               What figure of speech is in this line? _____

               How can one tell apart the Latin words for "faith" and "string/lyre?" _____
               _____

Lines 14–15   Why are *moderere* and *redeat* subjunctive? _____
               _____

Line 15   What is the case and use of *imagini?* _____

Line 16   What is the case and use of *virga?* _____

               What figure of speech is in this line? _____

Line 17   What is the case and use of *precibus?* _____

               What two figures of speech are in this line? _____

Line 18   What is the case and use of *gregi?* _____

Line 19   What figure of speech is in this line? _____

               What is the subject of *fit?* _____

Multiple Choice Questions *Suggested time: 15 minutes*

ergo Quintilium perpetuus sopor
urget? cui Pudor et Iustitiae soror,
incorrupta Fides nudaque Veritas
    quando ullum inveniet parem?

multis ille bonis flebilis occidit,   5
nulli flebilior, quam tibi, Vergili.
tu, frustra pius, heu, non ita creditum
    poscis Quintilium deos.

quid, si Threicio blandius Orpheo
auditam moderere arboribus fidem,   10
num vanae redeat sanguis imagini,
    quam virga semel horrida

non lenis precibus fata recludere
nigro compulerit Mercurius gregi?

1. The sister mentioned in line 2 is
   a. Faith
   c. Justice
   b. Modesty
   d. Truth

2. The case of *cui* (line 2) is determined by
   a. *soror* (line 2)
   c. *parem* (line 4)
   b. *inveniet* (line 4)
   d. *Quintilium* (line 1)

3. The tense and mood of *inveniet* (line 4) are
   a. present subjunctive
   c. present indicative
   b. perfect indicative
   d. future indicative

4. From lines 5–6, we learn that
   a. good men mourned no one more than they mourned Vergil
   c. many good men wept because of Vergil's grief
   b. Quintilius died of grief over many good men
   d. no one wept for Quintilius more than Vergil did

5. In line 5, *ille* refers to
   a. *Quintilium* (line 1)
   c. *parem* (line 4)
   b. *Vergili* (line 6)
   d. *nulli* (line 6)

6. The case and number of *flebilis* (line 5) are

   a. accusative plural

   b. nominative singular

   c. genitive singular

   d. dative plural

7. A figure of speech contained in line 5 is

   a. chiasmus

   b. hyperbole

   c. interlocked word order/synchysis

   d. oxymoron

8. From the words *non ita creditum poscis Quintilium* (lines 7–8), we learn that Vergil

   a. lost faith after Quintilius' death

   b. wants Quintilius back unreasonably

   c. does not demand Quintilius as he did before

   d. put his trust in Quintilius in vain

9. The form *moderere* (line 10) is

   a. present infinitive

   b. imperfect subjunctive

   c. imperative

   d. present subjunctive

10. From lines 9–11, we learn that

    a. poetry immortalizes the dead

    b. Quintilius was a greater poet than Orpheus

    c. no music can revive the dead

    d. Orpheus swore an oath to the trees

11. The case of *Orpheo* (line 9) is determined by

    a. *auditam* (line 10)

    b. *blandius* (line 9)

    c. *moderere* (line 10)

    d. *fidem* (line 10)

12. The best translation of line 13 (*lenis . . . recludere*) is

    a. to open up the fates with gentle prayers

    b. the fates for gentle prayers to open up

    c. to open up the gentle fates with prayers

    d. gentle to open up the fates to prayers

13. What did Mercury do to the *nigro . . . gregi* (line 14)?

    a. he opened the fates to it

    b. he compelled it to open up

    c. he drove Quintilius' shade into it

    d. he forced it to heed a virgin's prayers

Translation *Suggested time: 15 minutes*

Translate the passage below as literally as possible.

> ergo Quintilium perpetuus sopor
> urget? cui Pudor et Iustitiae soror,
> incorrupta Fides nudaque Veritas
>   quando ullum inveniet parem?
>
> multis ille bonis flebilis occidit,   5
> nulli flebilior, quam tibi, Vergili.
> tu, frustra pius, heu, non ita creditum
>   poscis Quintilium deos.

_____

_____

_____

_____

_____

_____

_____

_____

_____

_____

Short Analysis Questions *Suggested time: 10 minutes.*

Quis desiderio sit pudor aut modus
tam cari capitis? praecipe lugubris
cantus, Melpomene, cui liquidam pater
    vocem cum cithara dedit.

ergo Quintilium perpetuus sopor   5
urget? cui Pudor et Iusitiae soror,
incorrupta Fides nudaque Veritas
    quando ullum inveniet parem?

multis ille bonis flebilis occidit,
nulli flebilior, quam tibi, Vergili.   10
tu, frustra pius, heu, non ita creditum
    poscis Quintilium deos.

1.   What is the attitude toward Quintilius' death among those who knew him? Cite and translate two Latin words or phrases that illustrate this attitude.

    _____

    _____

2.   Name two qualities of character that the poem attributes to Quintilius. Cite and translate a Latin word or phrase that illustrates each quality.

    _____

    _____

3.   Name a figure of speech that occurs in lines 5–8 and write out the Latin word(s) that illustrate it.

    _____

4.   Identify one criticism that the poet makes of Vergil's reaction to Quintilius' death, and cite and translate or accurately paraphrase the Latin word or phrases that support your point.

    _____

    _____

Essay *Suggested time: 20 minutes.*

Quis desiderio sit pudor aut modus
tam cari capitis? praecipe lugubris
cantus, Melpomene, cui liquidam pater
    vocem cum cithara dedit.

ergo Quintilium perpetuus sopor   5
urget? cui Pudor et Iustitiae soror,
incorrupta Fides nudaque Veritas
    quando ullum inveniet parem?

multis ille bonis flebilis occidit,
nulli flebilior, quam tibi, Vergili.   10
tu, frustra pius, heu, non ita creditum
    poscis Quintilium deos.

quid, si Threicio blandius Orpheo
auditam moderere arboribus fidem,
num vanae redeat sanguis imagini,   15
    quam virga semel horrida

non lenis precibus fata recludere
nigro compulerit Mercurius gregi?
durum, sed levius fit patientia,
    quicquid corrigere est nefas.   20

The occasion of this poem is the death of Horace's and Vergil's friend, Quintilius. In a **short** essay, explain what Horace suggests poetry can and cannot do in response to the death of a loved one, and show how he conveys this message.

Support your assertions with references to the Latin text **throughout** the poem. All Latin words must be copied or their line numbers provided, AND they must be translated or paraphrased closely enough so that it is clear you understand the Latin. It is your responsibility to convince your reader that you are basing your conclusions on the Latin text and not merely on a general recollection of the passage. Direct your answer to the question; do not merely summarize the passage. Please write your essay on a separate piece of paper.

Scansion

Scan the following lines and name the meter.

multis ille bonis flebilis occidit,

nulli flebilior, quam tibi, Vergili.

tu, frustra pius, heu, non ita creditum

    poscis Quintilium deos.

quid, si Threicio blandius Orpheo   5

auditam moderere arboribus fidem,

num vanae redeat sanguis imagini,

    quam virga semel horrida

ODE 1.25

Parcius iunctas quatiunt fenestras
iactibus crebris iuvenes protervi,
nec tibi somnos adimunt, amatque
    ianua limen,

quae prius multum facilis movebat   5
cardines. audis minus et minus iam:
'me tuo longas pereunte noctes,
    Lydia, dormis?'

invicem moechos anus adrogantis
flebis in solo levis angiportu,   10
Thracio bacchante magis sub inter-
    lunia vento,

cum tibi flagrans amor et libido,
quae solet matres furiare equorum,
saeviet circa iecur ulcerosum,   15
    non sine questu,

laeta quod pubes hedera virenti
gaudeat pulla magis atque myrto,
aridas frondes hiemis sodali
    dedicet Hebro.   20

Short Answer Questions

Line 1   What form is *parcius,* and what does it modify? _____

                What is the subject of *quatiunt?* _____

Line 2   What is the case and use of *iactibus?* _____

                What figure of speech is in this line? _____

Lines 3–4   What two figures of speech are in these lines? _____

Line 5   What is the antecedent of *quae?* _____

Line 7   What is the case and use of *me?* _____

                What does *tuo* signify? _____

                What form is *pereunte,* and what does it modify? _____

Line 9   What is the case and use of *moechos?* _____

                 What is the case and use of *anus?* _____

                 What does *adrogantis* modify? _____

Line 10   What is the case and use of *levis?* _____

Line 12   What is the case and use of *vento?* _____

Line 13   Translate *cum.* _____

                 What figure of speech is in this line? _____

Line 14   What verb form is *furiare,* and how is it used grammatically in its context?_____

                 _____

                 What is the case and use of *equorum?* _____

Line15   What is the tense and the subject of *saeviet?* _____

                 What is the case and use of *iecur?* _____

Lines 14–16   What figure of speech is in these lines? _____

Line 17   What does *laeta* modify? _____

                 What is the case and use of *hedera?* _____

Line 19   What is the case and use of *hiemis?* _____

                 What is the case and use of *sodali?* _____

Line 20   What is the case and use of *Hebro?* _____

Multiple Choice Questions *Suggested time: 15 minutes.*

Parcius iunctas quatiunt fenestras
iactibus crebris iuvenes protervi,
nec tibi somnos adimunt, amatque
    ianua limen,

quae prius multum facilis movebat   5
cardines. audis minus et minus iam:
'me tuo longas pereunte noctes,
    Lydia, dormis?'

invicem moechos anus adrogantis
flebis in solo levis angiportu,   10
Thracio bacchante magis sub inter-
    lunia vento,

1. From lines 1–2, we learn that now youths
   - a. close and shake the windows
   - b. rarely throw stones at the shutters
   - c. seek joined windows
   - d. come in crowds to the windows

2. The case of *iactibus* (line 2) is determined by
   - a. *quatiunt* (line 1)
   - b. *crebris* (line 2)
   - c. *protervi* (line 2)
   - d. *parcius* (line 1)

3. From the words *amatque ianua limen* (lines 3–4), we may infer that
   - a. the doorkeeper loves his position
   - b. the doorframe fits snugly around the door
   - c. light shines on the door
   - d. the door rarely opens

4. A correct translation of the words *prius . . . cardines* (lines 5–6) is
   - a. a very easy hinge was moving
   - b. at the very beginning was moving easy hinges
   - c. formerly used to move its hinges very readily
   - d. was the first to move its hinges with ease

5. Lines 7–8 are spoken by Lydia's
   - a. lover
   - b. son
   - c. husband
   - d. servant

6. The experience that is long (line 7) is
   - a. the speaker's death
   - b. waiting for Lydia to open the door
   - c. a night spent with Lydia
   - d. Lydia's listening at the door

7. In line 9, *invicem* signals a reversal of roles between
   a. the old woman and adulterers
   b. Lydia and old women
   c. the speaker of lines 7–8 and adulterers
   d. Lydia and her lovers

8. The case and number of *adrogantis* (line 9) are
   a. genitive singular
   b. accusative plural
   c. ablative plural
   d. nominative singular

9. A figure of speech contained in line 10 is
   a. transferred epithet
   b. chiasmus
   c. prolepsis
   d. hendiadys

10. In line 10, *levis* modifies
    a. *moechos* (line 9)
    b. *adrogantis* (line 9)
    c. *angiportu* (line 10)
    d. the subject of *flebis* (line 10)

11. The best translation of *solo* (line 10) is
    a. usual
    b. sunny
    c. lonely
    d. earthy

12. In line 11, *bacchante* describes
    a. a Thracian
    b. Lydia
    c. the wind
    d. the moon

Translation *Suggested time: 15 minutes*

Translate the passage below as literally as possible.

> invicem moechos anus adrogantis
> flebis in solo levis angiportu,
> Thracio bacchante magis sub inter-
>   lunia vento,
>
> cum tibi flagrans amor et libido,   5
> quae solet matres furiare equorum,
> saeviet circa iecur ulcerosum,
>   non sine questu,

_____

_____

_____

_____

_____

_____

_____

_____

_____

_____

Short Analysis Questions *Suggested time: 10 minutes*

cum tibi flagrans amor et libido,
quae solet matres furiare equorum,
saeviet circa iecur ulcerosum,
   non sine questu,

laeta quod pubes hedera virenti   5
gaudeat pulla magis atque myrto,
aridas frondes hiemis sodali
   dedicet Hebro.

1. To what is Lydia compared in line 2? What does this comparison say about her character?

    _____

    _____

    _____

2. In line 3 (*saeviet circa iecur ulcerosum*),

   a. why does mention of the bodily organ, *iecur,* fit this context?

      _____

      _____

   b. what is the significance of *ulcerosum* as a description of Lydia?

      _____

      _____

3. Write out and scan line 3.

    _____

4. Name a figure of speech that appears in line 4, and write out the Latin that illustrates it.

    _____

5. In lines 5–8, the speaker contrasts dry leaves to two other plants. **Briefly,**

   a. identify these plants (and)

      _____

   b. show how the contrast contributes to the speaker's point about Lydia.

      _____

      _____

Essay *Suggested time: 20 minutes.*

Parcius iunctas quatiunt fenestras
iactibus crebris iuvenes protervi,
nec tibi somnos adimunt, amatque
    ianua limen,

quae prius multum facilis movebat   5
cardines. audis minus et minus iam:
'me tuo longas pereunte noctes,
    Lydia, dormis?'

invicem moechos anus adrogantis
flebis in solo levis angiportu,   10
Thracio bacchante magis sub inter-
    lunia vento,

cum tibi flagrans amor et libido,
quae solet matres furiare equorum,
saeviet circa iecur ulcerosum,   15
    non sine questu,

laeta quod pubes hedera virenti
gaudeat pulla magis atque myrto,
aridas frondes hiemis sodali
    dedicet Hebro.   20

In this ode, a speaker delivers invective, or verbal abuse, against Lydia. In a short essay, discuss how the speaker uses references to present, past, and future to help convey his invective.

Support your assertions with references to the Latin text **throughout** the poem. All Latin words must be copied or their line numbers provided, AND they must be translated or paraphrased closely enough so that it is clear you understand the Latin. It is your responsibility to convince your reader that you are basing your conclusions on the Latin text and not merely on a general recollection of the passage. Direct your answer to the question; do not merely summarize the passage. Please write your essay on a separate piece of paper.

Scansion

Scan the following lines and name the meter.

cum tibi flagrans amor et libido,

quae solet matres furiare equorum,

saeviet circa iecur ulcerosum,

    non sine questu,

laeta quod pubes hedera virenti   5

gaudeat pulla magis atque myrto,

aridas frondes hiemis sodali

    dedicet Hebro.

ODE 1.37

Nunc est bibendum, nunc pede libero
pulsanda tellus, nunc Saliaribus
    ornare pulvinar deorum
        tempus erat dapibus, sodales.

antehac nefas depromere Caecubum   5
cellis avitis, dum Capitolio
    regina dementis ruinas
        funus et imperio parabat

contaminato cum grege turpium
morbo virorum, quidlibet inpotens   10
    sperare fortunaque dulci
        ebria; sed minuit furorem

vix una sospes navis ab ignibus,
mentemque lymphatam Mareotico
    redegit in veros timores   15
        Caesar ab Italia volantem

remis adurgens, accipiter velut
mollis columbas aut leporem citus
    venator in campis nivalis
        Haemoniae, daret ut catenis   20

fatale monstrum, quae generosius
perire quaerens nec muliebriter
    expavit ensem, nec latentis
        classe cita reparavit oras,

ausa et iacentem visere regiam   25
voltu sereno, fortis et asperas
    tractare serpentes, ut atrum
        corpore combiberet venenum,

deliberata morte ferocior:
saevis Liburnis scilicet invidens   30
    privata deduci superbo
        non humilis mulier triumpho.

Short Answer Questions.

Line 1   What is the case and use of *pede libero?* _____

Line 3   On what words in the sentence does *ornare* depend? _____

              What is the case and use of *pulvinar?* _____

Line 4   What is the case and use of *dapibus?* _____

Lines 1–4   What four figures of speech are in the first stanza? _____
_____

Line 5   What figure of speech is in this line? _____

              What is the case and use of *nefas?* _____

              On what word does *depromere* depend? _____

Line 6   What is the case and use of *cellis?* _____

              What is the case and use of *Capitolio?* _____

Line 8   What figure of speech (non-AP) is in this line? _____

              What is the case and use of *funus?* _____

              What is the case and use of *imperio?* _____

Line 9   What is the case and use of *grege?* _____

Line 10   What is the case and use of *morbo?* _____

              What is the case and use of *quidlibet?* _____

              What does *inpotens* modify? _____

Line 11   What is the case and use of *fortuna?* _____

Lines 11–12   What figure of speech is in these lines? _____

Line 13   What figure of speech is in this line? _____

Line 14   Of what verb is *mentem* the object, and what is the subject of that verb? _____
_____

              What is the case and use of *Mareotico?* _____

Line 16   What figure of speech is in this line? _____

Line 17   What is the case and use of *remis?* _____

              What figure of speech (non-AP) is in this line? _____

Lines 17–20   What figure of speech is in these lines? _____

Line 18   What is the case and use of *mollis?* _____

Line 19   What is the case and use of *nivalis?* _____

Line 20   What is the case and use of *catenis?* _____

Lines 18–20   Of what verb are *accipiter* and *venator* the subjects? _____

Line 21   What form is *generosius?* _____

Line 23   What does *latentis* modify? _____

Line 24   What is the case and use of *classe?* _____

Line 26   What is the case and use of *voltu* and what is another spelling of this word? _____
                 _____

                 What figure of speech (non-AP) is in this line? _____
                 _____

Line 29   What is the case and use of *morte?* _____

Line 30   What two figures of speech are in this line? _____

Line 31   What is the case and use of *privata?* _____

                 What figure of speech (non-AP) is in this line? _____

Lines 31–32   What three figures of speech are in these lines? _____
                 _____

Multiple Choice Questions *Suggested time: 15 minutes*

fatale monstrum, quae generosius
perire quaerens nec muliebriter
   expavit ensem, nec latentis
     classe cita reparavit oras,

ausa et iacentem visere regiam   5
voltu sereno, fortis et asperas
   tractare serpentes, ut atrum
     corpore combiberet venenum.

deliberata morte ferocior:
saevis Liburnis scilicet invidens   10
   privata deduci superbo
     non humilis mulier triumpho.

1.   In line 1, *fatale monstrum* is a reference to
    a. the Minotaur   b. Marc Antony
    c. the Egyptian bull god   d. Cleopatra

2. The words *quae . . . ensem* (lines 1–3) are translated

    a. which, generously seeking to die, did not fear a woman's sword

    b. who, seeking to perish more nobly, neither panicked like a woman at a sword

    c. and which the son-in-law, seeking to go through, did not, as a woman would, fear the sword

    d. who, dying with more dignity, did not dread the sword as a woman

3. From lines 3–4, we learn that Cleopatra did not

    a. prepare oars for her fleet

    b. repair the prows of her ships

    c. make her fleet ready secretly

    d. sail to secluded regions

4. The case of *classe* (line 4) is determined by

    a. *cita* (line 4)

    b. *latentis* (line 3)

    c. *reparavit* (line 4)

    d. *oras* (line 4)

5. The form of the word *visere* (line 5) is

    a. present infinitive

    b. perfect indicative

    c. present imperative

    d. present indicative

6. In line 6, *voltu sereno* is an ablative

    a. absolute

    b. of means

    c. of cause

    d. of manner

7. Lines 5–6 state that Cleopatra

    a. saw the queen lying with a serene face calm face

    b. dared to throw queenly looks from her

    c. did not shrink from going to her ruined palace

    d. calmly faced danger while resting in her palace

8. In line 6, *fortis* modifies

    a. *regiam* (line 5)

    b. *serpentes* (line 7)

    c. the person described as *ausa* (line 5)

    d. *voltu* (line 6)

9. In line 7, the word *ut* is translated

    a. with the result that

    b. in order to

    c. as

    d. that

10. A figure of speech found in line 8 is

    a. metaphor

    b. zeugma

    c. simile

    d. oxymoron

11. The case and number of *deliberata* (line 9) are

    a. accusative plural

    b. nominative singular

    c. nominative plural

    d. ablative singular

12. From line 9, we learn that Cleopatra was ferocious

    a. more than death

    b. with the force of death

    c. when she decided to die

    d. against death

13. The words *scilicet invidens privata deduci* (lines 10–11) are translated

    a. evidently refusing to be escorted as a private person

    b. if it is allowed for private things to be brought down

    c. of course envying a private woman being led down

    d. of course, having been deprived, she was led down unseen

Translation *Suggested time: 15 minutes*

Translate the passage below as literally as possible.

> Nunc est bibendum, nunc pede libero
> pulsanda tellus, nunc Saliaribus
>   ornare pulvinar deorum
>   tempus erat dapibus, sodales.
>
> antehac nefas depromere Caecubum   5
> cellis avitis, dum Capitolio
>   regina dementis ruinas
>   funus et imperio parabat

_____

_____

_____

_____

_____

_____

_____

_____

_____

Short Analysis Questions *Suggested time: 10 minutes*

remis adurgens, accipiter velut
mollis columbas aut leporem citus
   venator in campis nivalis
      Haemoniae, daret ut catenis

fatale monstrum, quae generosius   5
perire quaerens nec muliebriter
   expavit ensem, nec latentis
      classe cita reparavit oras,

1. The simile of stanza one involves hunters and their prey.

   a. Write out and translate the Latin words that denote the hunters and the prey.

   b. Which historical personage is represented by the hunters, and which historical personage is represented by the prey?

   c. According to the passage, for what reason did the one historical personage pursue the other? Cite and translate or paraphrase the Latin words that support your answer.

2. Line 5 contains a shift in gender between words that refer to the same person.

   a. Citing the Latin, identify and explain this shift.

   b. How does this shift help the poet develop his image of the person concerned? Support your statement by referring to the Latin text.

3. Write out and scan line 8 (*classe . . . oras*).

Essay *Suggested time: 20 minutes.*

Nunc est bibendum, nunc pede libero
pulsanda tellus, nunc Saliaribus
   ornare pulvinar deorum
      tempus erat dapibus, sodales.

antehac nefas depromere Caecubum   5
cellis avitis, dum Capitolio
   regina dementis ruinas
      funus et imperio parabat

contaminato cum grege turpium
morbo virorum, quidlibet inpotens   10
   sperare fortunaque dulci
      ebria; sed minuit furorem

vix una sospes navis ab ignibus,
mentemque lymphatam Mareotico
   redegit in veros timores   15
      Caesar ab Italia volantem

remis adurgens, . . .

The ode from which these lines are excerpted was written in commemoration of the victory of Octavian/Augustus Caesar over Cleopatra. In a **short,** well-organized essay, describe the attitude that is expressed in the quoted passage toward this victory, and show how Horace conveys this attitude.

Support your assertions with references to the Latin text **throughout** the passage quoted above. All Latin words must be copied or their line numbers provided, AND they must be translated or paraphrased closely enough so that it is clear you understand the Latin. It is your responsibility to convince your reader that you are basing your conclusions on the Latin text and not merely on a general recollection of the passage. Direct your answer to the question; do not merely summarize the passage. Please write your essay on a separate piece of paper.

Scansion

Scan the following lines and name the meter.

fatale monstrum, quae generosius

perire quaerens nec muliebriter

expavit ensem, nec latentis

classe cita reparavit oras,

ausa et iacentem visere regiam   5

voltu sereno, fortis et asperas

tractare serpentes, ut atrum

corpore combiberet venenum.

ODE 1.38

Persicos odi, puer, apparatus,
displicent nexae philyra coronae;
mitte sectari, rosa quo locorum
    sera moretur.

simplici myrto nihil adlabores   5
sedulus, curo: neque te ministrum
dedecet myrtus, neque me sub arta
    vite bibentem.

Short Answer Questions

Lines 1–2   What figure of speech is in these lines? _____

Line 2   What is the case and use of *philyra?* _____

Line 3   What is the translation of *mitte sectari?* _____

                     What is the case and use of *locorum?*_____

Line 5   What is the case and use of *myrto?* _____

                     What is the case and use of *nihil?* _____

Lines 6–7   What two figures of speech are in these lines? _____

Line 7   What does *arta* modify?_____

Line 8   What is the case and use of *vite?* _____

Line 9   What does *bibentem* modify? _____

Multiple Choice Questions *Suggested time: 13 minutes*

Persicos odi, puer, apparatus,
displicent nexae philyra coronae;
mitte sectari, rosa quo locorum
    sera moretur.

simplici myrto nihil adlabores   5
sedulus, curo: neque te ministrum
dedecet myrtus, neque me sub arta
    vite bibentem.

1. Line 1 (*Persicos . . . apparatus*) is translated
    a. I hate, boy, Persian magnificence
    b. Boy, hate Persian paraphernalia
    c. I hated Persian pomp, boy
    d. Be prepared, boy, to hate the Persians

2. The case and number of *apparatus* (line 1) are
    a. nominative singular
    b. accusative plural
    c. genitive singular
    d. vocative singular

3. The adjective *Persicos* is appropriate for use in line 1 because Persia was proverbial for
    a. archery
    b. warfare
    c. luxury
    d. deceit

4. The case of *philyra* (line 2) is determined by
    a. *coronae* (line 2)
    b. *nexae* (line 2)
    c. *apparatus* (line 1)
    d. *displicent* (line 2)

5. The words *rosa . . . moretur* (lines 3–4) are translated
    a. where the rosy evening passes away
    b. in what place the evening rose tarries
    c. by which the last rose of the places is delayed
    d. to the place where the late rose lingers

6. The tense and mood of *moretur* (line 4) are
    a. present subjunctive
    b. future indicative
    c. present indicative
    d. imperfect subjunctive

7. From lines 5–6, we learn that the speaker does not want the *puer* to
    a. do no work
    b. look for more than myrtle
    c. stop at simple tasks
    d. sit simply and work

8. In line 5, *simplici* modifies

   a. the subject of *adlabores* (line 5)   b. *nihil* (line 5)

   c. the subject of *curo* (line 6)   d. *myrto* (line 5)

9. A figure of speech contained in lines 6–7 is

   a. synecdoche   b. metaphor

   c. transferred epithet   d. anaphora

10. In lines 6–8, the *puer* is envisioned as

    a. decently clothed   b. drinking wine

    c. wearing myrtle   d. beneath a vine

11. From the words *arta vite* (lines 7–8), we may infer that the vine

    a. is artfully entwined on a trellis   b. has dense leaves

    c. has numerous limbs   d. grows high overhead

Translation *Suggested time: 15 minutes*

Translate the passage below as literally as possible.

> **Persicos odi, puer, apparatus,**
> **displicent nexae philyra coronae;**
> **mitte sectari, rosa quo locorum**
>   **sera moretur.**
>
> **simplici myrto nihil adlabores**   5
> **sedulus, curo: neque te ministrum**
> **dedecet myrtus, neque me sub arta**
>   **vite bibentem.**

_____

_____

_____

_____

_____

_____

_____

_____

_____

Short Analysis Questions *Suggested time: 10 minutes.*

Persicos odi, puer, apparatus,
displicent nexae philyra coronae;
mitte sectari, rosa quo locorum
    sera moretur.

simplici myrto nihil adlabores   5
sedulus, curo: neque te ministrum
dedecet myrtus, neque me sub arta
    vite bibentem.

1.   Enumerate three things the speaker tells the boy he does not want. Copy and translate the
       Latin words that denote them.

       _____

       _____

2.   Identify a figure of speech that is found in the first stanza, and copy the Latin words that illus-
       trate it.

       _____

3.   a.   Of what plant does the speaker approve? _____

       b.   What does he tell the boy to do with this plant?

               _____

               _____

       c.   What reason does he give for these instructions?

               _____

               _____

4.   Copy and scan line 2 (*displicent . . . coronae*).

       _____

Essay *Suggested time: 20 minutes*

Persicos odi, puer, apparatus,
displicent nexae philyra coronae;
mitte sectari, rosa quo locorum
    sera moretur.

simplici myrto nihil adlabores   5
sedulus, curo: neque te ministrum
dedecet myrtus, neque me sub arta
    vite bibentem.

Readers of this poem have made various attempts to identify the principles or values to which the poet commits himself. In a short, well-organized essay, set forth your view about the principles that the ode expresses and show how the poet conveys them.

Support your assertions with references to the Latin text **throughout** the poem. All Latin words must be copied or their line numbers provided, AND they must be translated or paraphrased closely enough so that it is clear you understand the Latin. It is your responsibility to convince your reader that you are basing your conclusions on the Latin text and not merely on a general recollection of the passage. Direct your answer to the question; do not merely summarize the passage.

Scansion

Scan the following lines and name the meter.

Persicos odi, puer, apparatus,

displicent nexae philyra coronae;

mitte sectari, rosa quo locorum

    sera moretur.

simplici myrto nihil adlabores   5

sedulus, curo: neque te ministrum

dedecet myrtus, neque me sub arta

    vite bibentem.

ODE 2.3

Aequam memento rebus in arduis
servare mentem, non secus in bonis
    ab insolenti temperatam
      laetitia, moriture Delli,

seu maestus omni tempore vixeris,   5
seu te in remoto gramine per dies
    festos reclinatum bearis
      interiore nota Falerni.

quo pinus ingens albaque populus
umbram hospitalem consociare amant   10
    ramis? quid obliquo laborat
      lympha fugax trepidare rivo?

huc vina et unguenta et nimium brevis
flores amoenae ferre iube rosae,
    dum res et aetas et sororum   15
      fila trium patiuntur atra.

cedes coemptis saltibus et domo
villaque, flavos quam Tiberis lavit,
    cedes, et exstructis in altum
      divitiis potietur heres.   20

divesne prisco natus ab Inacho,
nil interest, an pauper et infima
    de gente sub divo moreris,
      victima nil miserantis Orci:

omnes eodem cogimur, omnium   25
versatur urna serius ocius
    sors exitura et nos in aeternum
      exilium inpositura cumbae.

Short Answer Questions

Line 2   What verb form is *servare*, and how is it used grammatically in its context? _____
_____

Lines 1–2   What two figures of speech are in these lines? _____

Line 4   What is the case and use of *Delli?* _____

Line 7   What does *reclinatum* modify? _____

Line 8   What figure of speech is in this line? _____

                What is the case and use of *nota?* _____

Lines 9–10   What figure of speech is in these lines? _____

Line 11   What is the case and use of *ramis?* _____

                What figure of speech is in this line? _____

Line 15   What is the case and reason of *sororum?* _____

Line 16   What does *atra* modify? _____

Line 17   What is the case and use of *saltibus?* _____

                What is the case and use of *domo?* _____

Line 18   What is the case and use of *villa?* _____

Line 21   What does *natus* modify? _____

Line 22   What is the subject of *nil interest?* _____

Lines 21–22   How are *ne . . . an* translated? _____

Line 24   What is the case and use of *nil?* _____

                What does *miserantis* modify? _____

                What is the case and use of *Orci?* _____

Line 26   What is the subject of *versatur?* _____

Line 27   What does *exitura* modify? _____

                What is the case and use of *nos?* _____

Line 28   What is the case and use of *exilium?* _____

                What does *inpositura* modify? _____

                What figure of speech is in this line? _____

Lines 26–28   What figure of speech is in these lines? _____

Multiple Choice Questions *Suggested time: 15 minutes*

quo pinus ingens albaque populus
umbram hospitalem consociare amant
   ramis? quid obliquo laborat
     lympha fugax trepidare rivo?

huc vina et unguenta et nimium brevis   5
flores amoenae ferre iube rosae,
   dum res et aetas et sororum
     fila trium patiuntur atra.

cedes coemptis saltibus et domo
villaque, flavos quam Tiberis lavit,   10
   cedes, et exstructis in altum
     divitiis potietur heres.

1. In line 1, *quo* is translated
   a. by what
   c. to where
   b. to what purpose
   d. by which

2. A figure of speech that is contained in line 1 is
   a. transferred epithet
   c. interlocked word order/synchysis
   b. hendiadys
   d. chiasmus

3. From the words *quo . . . ramis* (lines 1–3) we learn that
   a. public associations gladly care for the sick
   c. the huge population loves to gather among the pines
   b. the pine grows close to the poplar
   d. the poplar shades the pine as its guest

4. The case of *ramis* (line 3) is determined by
   a. *consociare* (line 2)
   c. *hospitalem* (line 2)
   b. *amant* (line 2)
   d. *umbram* (line 2)

5. The thing that "labors" in line 3 is a
   a. fluid in the body
   c. drink
   b. runaway slave
   d. brook

6. The items enumerated in line 5 are preparations for a
   a. drinking party
   c. religious festival
   b. wedding
   d. voyage

7. In line 5, *nimium* modifies

    a. *ferre* (line 6)   b. *iube* (line 6)

    c. *brevis* (line 5)   d. *amoenae* (line 6)

8. In line 7, *aetas* is translated

    a. summer   b. life

    c. tide   d. heat

9. In line 7, *sororum* refers to the

    a. Muses   b. Graces

    c. Fates   d. Hours

10. The case and number of *atra* (line 8) are

    a. nominative plural   b. ablative singular

    c. accusative plural   d. nominative singular

11. From lines 9–12 (*cedes . . . heres*), we learn that the addressee will

    a. go bankrupt   b. surrender

    c. bequeath property   d. emigrate

12. The words *exstructis . . . potietur* (lines 11–12) are translated

    a. gains control of the wealth built out into the deep   b. gets possession of the rich structures extending into the sea

    c. will allow the wealth to be piled up on high   d. will gain possession of the riches piled on high

Translation *Suggested time: 15 minutes*

Translate the passage below as literally as possible.

> Aequam memento rebus in arduis
> servare mentem, non secus in bonis
>   ab insolenti temperatam
>   laetitia, moriture Delli,
>
> seu maestus omni tempore vixeris,   5
> seu te in remoto gramine per dies
>   festos reclinatum bearis
>   interiore nota Falerni.

_____

_____

_____

_____

_____

_____

_____

_____

_____

Short Analysis Questions *Suggested time: 10 minutes.*

divesne prisco natus ab Inacho,
nil interest, an pauper et infima
  de gente sub divo moreris,
    victima nil miserantis Orci:

omnes eodem cogimur, omnium   5
versatur urna serius ocius
  sors exitura et nos in aeternum
    exilium inpositura cumbae.

1. Two sets of personal characteristics are said to "make no difference" (*nil interest,* line 2).

   a. Identify these characteristics and cite the Latin words that refer to them.

      _____

      _____

   b. Why do these characteristics make no difference?

      _____

      _____

2. Write out and scan line 3.

      _____

3. Who is Orcus, and why is this character described as *nil miserantis* (line 4)?

      _____

      _____

4. Lines 6–8 develop an image of the *sors.*

   a. What is a *sors*?

      _____

   b. What does it represent as it is presented in the image?

      _____

Essay *Suggested time: 20 minutes*

Aequam memento rebus in arduis
servare mentem, non secus in bonis
   ab insolenti temperatam
      laetitia, moriture Delli,

seu maestus omni tempore vixeris,   5
seu te in remoto gramine per dies
   festos reclinatum bearis
      interiore nota Falerni.

quo pinus ingens albaque populus
umbram hospitalem consociare amant   10
   ramis? quid obliquo laborat
      lympha fugax trepidare rivo?

huc vina et unguenta et nimium brevis
flores amoenae ferre iube rosae,
   dum res et aetas et sororum   15
      fila trium patiuntur atra.

Much of this ode is composed of references to the natural world. In a short, well-organized essay, discuss how Horace's nature references help him develop the advice about life that he gives Dellius.

Support your assertions with references to the Latin text **throughout** the passage. All Latin words must be copied or their line numbers provided, AND they must be translated or paraphrased closely enough so that it is clear you understand the Latin. It is your responsibility to convince your reader that you are basing your conclusions on the Latin text and not merely on a general recollection of the passage. Direct your answer to the question; do not merely summarize the passage. Please write your essay on a separate piece of paper.

Scansion

Scan the following lines and name the meter.

huc vina et unguenta et nimium brevis

flores amoenae ferre iube rosae,

    dum res et aetas et sororum

        fila trium patiuntur atra.

cedes coemptis saltibus et domo   5

villaque, flavos quam Tiberis lavit,

    cedes, et exstructis in altum

        divitiis potietur heres.

ODE 2.7

O saepe mecum tempus in ultimum
deducte Bruto militiae duce,
    quis te redonavit Quiritem
        dis patriis Italoque caelo,

Pompei, meorum prime sodalium,   5
cum quo morantem saepe diem mero
    fregi coronatus nitentis
        malobathro Syrio capillos?

tecum Philippos et celerem fugam
sensi relicta non bene parmula,   10
    cum fracta virtus et minaces
        turpe solum tetigere mento.

sed me per hostis Mercurius celer
denso paventem sustulit aere,
    te rursus in bellum resorbens   15
        unda fretis tulit aestuosis.

ergo obligatam redde Iovi dapem,
longaque fessum militia latus
    depone sub lauru mea, nec
        parce cadis tibi destinatis.   20

oblivioso levia Massico
ciboria exple, funde capacibus
    unguenta de conchis. quis udo
        deproperare apio coronas

curatve myrto? quem Venus arbitrum   25
dicet bibendi? non ego sanius
    bacchabor Edonis: recepto
        dulce mihi furere est amico.

Short Answer Questions

Line 2   What is the case and use of *deducte*? _____

          What is the case and use of *militiae*? _____

Line 4	What figure of speech is in this line? _____
	What is the case and use of *dis*? _____
Line 5	What is the case and use of *Pompei*? _____
Line 6	What figure of speech is in this line? _____
	What is the case and use of *mero*? _____
Line 6–7	What figure of speech is in these lines? _____
Lines 7–8	What is the figure of speech in these lines? _____
Line 11	What two figures of speech are in this line? _____
	What is the case and use of *minaces*? _____
Line 12	The verb *tetigere* is an alternative of what verb form? _____
	What figure of speech is in this line? _____
	What is the case and use of *mento*? _____
Line 13	What is the case and use of *me*? _____
Line 14	What does *paventem* modify? _____
	What is the case and use of *aere*? _____
Line 16	What is the case and use of *fretis*? _____
Lines 14–16	What figure of speech is in these lines? _____
Line 17	What is the case and use of *Iovi*? _____
Line 18	What figure of speech is in this line? _____
	What is the case and use of *militia*? _____
	What is the case and use of *latus*? _____
Line 20	What is the figure of speech in this line? _____
	What is the case and use of *cadis*? _____
Line 22	What figure of speech is in this line? _____
Lines 21–22	What figure of speech is in these lines? _____
Line 24	On what other word in the sentence does *deproperare* depend? _____
	What is the case and use of *apio*? _____
Line 25	What two words does *-ve* contrast? _____
	What is the case and use of *myrto*? _____
	What is the case and use of *arbitrum*? _____

Line 26   What is the form of *bibendi*? _____

                What figure of speech is in this line? _____

Line 27   What is the case and use of *Edonis?*_____

Line 28   What is the case and use of *mihi?* _____

                What is the subject of *est?* _____

                What is the case and use of *amico?* _____

Multiple Choice Questions *Suggested time: 15 minutes*

Pompei, meorum prime sodalium,
cum quo morantem saepe diem mero
    fregi coronatus nitentis
        malobathro Syrio capillos?

tecum Philippos et celerem fugam   5
sensi relicta non bene parmula,
    cum fracta virtus et minaces
        turpe solum tetigere mento.

sed me per hostis Mercurius celer
denso paventem sustulit aere,   10
    te rursus in bellum resorbens
        unda fretis tulit aestuosis.

1.   A figure of speech contained in line 1 is
    a. hyperbole   b. interlocked word order/synchysis
    c. transferred epithet   d. asyndeton

2.   The translation of *quo* (line 2) is
    a. what   b. to where
    c. whom   d. which

3.   From lines 2–3, we learn that Horace and Pompeius used to drink
    a. during the day   b. watered-down wine
    c. together rarely   d. beginning at dusk

4.   In line 3, *coronatus* modifies
    a. *Pompei* (line 1)   b. *nitentis* (line 3)
    c. *capillos* (line 4)   d. the subject of *fregi* (line 3)

5. The case of *capillos* (line 4) is determined by
   a. *malobathro* (line 4)
   b. *coronatus* (line 3)
   c. *nitentis* (line 3)
   d. *fregi* (line 3)

6. The words *celerem . . . parmula* (lines 5–6) are translated
   a. I did not hear the swift flight well when I left my little shield behind
   b. I perceived well the swift flight and the little shield not left behind
   c. I experienced the swift flight, having basely left my little shield behind
   d. I did not understand the swift flight well, nor how my little shield was abandoned

7. Lines 7–8 refer to the defeat of the forces of
   a. Brutus and Cassius
   b. Antony and Cleopatra
   c. Pompey and the senate
   d. Pompey's sons

8. The translation of *solum* (line 8) is
   a. alone
   b. only
   c. the ground
   d. the accustomed

9. The form of the word *tetigere* (line 8) is
   a. present infinitive
   b. perfect indicative
   c. present indicative
   d. perfect participle

10. From lines 9–10, we learn that Horace
    a. escaped battle safely
    b. was pursued by a god
    c. feared the hostility of Mercury
    d. fled in a fog on the pavement

11. In line 10, *sustulit* is a form of
    a. *fero*
    b. *sustulo*
    c. *tollo*
    d. *surgo*

12. From lines 11–12, we can infer that Pompeius
    a. never saw Horace again
    b. was shipwrecked
    c. sailed during the summer
    d. fought longer than Horace did

13. The subject of *tulit* (line 12) is
    a. *Mercurius* (line 9)
    b. *hostis* (line 9)
    c. *rursus* (line 11)
    d. *unda* (line 12)

Translation *Suggested time: 15 minutes*

Translate the passage below as literally as possible.

> oblivioso levia Massico
> ciboria exple, funde capacibus
>   unguenta de conchis. quis udo
>   deproperare apio coronas
>
> curatve myrto? quem Venus arbitrum   5
> dicet bibendi? non ego sanius
>   bacchabor Edonis: recepto
>   dulce mihi furere est amico.

_____

_____

_____

_____

_____

_____

_____

_____

_____

_____

Short Analysis Questions *Suggested time: 10 minutes*

ergo obligatam redde Iovi dapem,
longaque fessum militia latus
    depone sub lauru mea, nec
        parce cadis tibi destinatis.

oblivioso levia Massico   5
ciboria exple, funde capacibus
    unguenta de conchis. quis udo
        deproperare apio coronas

curatve myrto? . . .

1.   a.   Why does the speaker want a banquet?

          _____

    b.   Why does he say it is owed to Jupiter?

          _____

2.   What are two things the speaker tells the addressee to do in lines 2–4? Write out the Latin word(s) that support your answer.

          _____

          _____

          _____

3.   Write out and scan line 3.

          _____

4.   What is the significance of the adjective *oblivioso* (line 5) in its context?

          _____

5.   a.   What does the speaker want in lines 7–9?

          _____

    b.   For what purpose does he want this?

          _____

Essay *Suggested time: 20 minutes*

O saepe mecum tempus in ultimum
deducte Bruto militiae duce,
    quis te redonavit Quiritem
        dis patriis Italoque caelo,

Pompei, meorum prime sodalium,   **5**
cum quo morantem saepe diem mero
    fregi coronatus nitentis
        malobathro Syrio capillos?

tecum Philippos et celerem fugam
sensi relicta non bene parmula,   **10**
    cum fracta virtus et minaces
        turpe solum tetigere mento.

. . . .

. . . quem Venus arbitrum
dicet bibendi? non ego sanius
    bacchabor Edonis: recepto   **15**
        dulce mihi furere est amico.

In the above excerpts, Horace rejoices at the return of his friend, Pompeius. In a short, well-organized essay, discuss the ways in which Horace in this passage shows what Pompeius means to him as a friend.

Support your assertions with references to the Latin text **throughout** the quoted passage. All Latin words must be copied or their line numbers provided, AND they must be translated or paraphrased closely enough so that it is clear you understand the Latin. It is your responsibility to convince your reader that you are basing your conclusions on the Latin text and not merely on a general recollection of the passage. Direct your answer to the question; do not merely summarize the passage. Please write your essay on a separate piece of paper.

Scansion

Scan the following lines and name the meter.

Pompei, meorum prime sodalium,
cum quo morantem saepe diem mero
    fregi coronatus nitentis
        malobathro Syrio capillos?

tecum Philippos et celerem fugam   5
sensi relicta non bene parmula,
    cum fracta virtus et minaces
        turpe solum tetigere mento.

ODE 2.10

Rectius vives, Licini, neque altum
semper urgendo, neque—dum procellas
cautus horrescis—nimium premendo
    litus iniquum.

auream quisquis mediocritatem   5
diligit, tutus caret obsoleti
sordibus tecti, caret invidenda
    sobrius aula.

saepius ventis agitatur ingens
pinus et celsae graviore casu   10
decidunt turres feriuntque summos
    fulgura montis.

sperat infestis, metuit secundis
alteram sortem bene praeparatum
pectus. informis hiemes reducit   15
    Iuppiter, idem

submovet. non, si male nunc, et olim
sic erit: quondam cithara tacentem
suscitat Musam, neque semper arcum
    tendit Apollo.   20

rebus angustis animosus atque
fortis appare: sapienter idem
contrahes vento nimium secundo
    turgida vela.

Short Answer Questions

Line 1   What tense is *vives?* _____

Line 2   What is the case and use of *urgendo,* and what is its object? _____
               _____

Line 3   What is the case and use of *premendo,* and what is its object? _____
               _____

Line 7   What is the case and use of *sordibus?* _____

                What is the case and use of *tecti?* _____

                _____

                What is the case, use, and literal translation of *invidenda?* _____

                _____

Line 9   What is the case and use of *ventis?* _____

Line 10   What is the case and use of *graviore casu?* _____

Line 11   What is the subject of *feriunt?* _____

Line 11–12   What is the translation of *summos montis?* _____

Lines 9–12   What figure of speech is in these lines? _____

Line 13   What two figures of speech are in this line? _____

Line 15   What does *informis* modify? _____

Lines 13–15   What figure of speech is in these lines? _____

Line 16   What is the case, use, and translation of *idem?* _____

Line 17   What is the object of *submovet?* _____

Line 18   What is the subject of *erit?* _____

                What is the case and use of *cithara?* _____

Line 19   What is the subject of *suscitat?* _____

Line 22   What is the case and use of *fortis?* _____

                What is the form of *appare?* _____

                What is the case and use of *idem?* _____

Line 23   What is the object of *contrahes?* _____

                What is the case and use of *vento?* _____

Lines 23–24   What figure of speech is in these lines? _____

Multiple Choice Questions *Suggested time: 15 minutes*

auream quisquis mediocritatem
diligit, tutus caret obsoleti
sordibus tecti, caret invidenda
    sobrius aula.

saepius ventis agitatur ingens   5
pinus et celsae graviore casu
decidunt turres feriuntque summos
    fulgura montis.

sperat infestis, metuit secundis
alteram sortem bene praeparatum   10
pectus. informis hiemes reducit
    Iuppiter, idem

submovet. . . .

1. The words *quisquis mediocritatem diligit* (lines 1–2) are translated
   a. whatever mediocrity loves
   b. whoever chooses the mean
   c. who selects the middle road
   d. whoever esteems moderation

2. In line 1, *auream* symbolizes
   a. breezes
   b. air
   c. excellence
   d. listening

3. The words *caret . . . aula* (lines 3–4) warn against
   a. excessive sobriety
   b. feeling envious
   c. the wine jar
   d. a sumptuous residence

4. In the imagery of lines 5–8, danger threatens things that are too
   a. weak
   b. heavy
   c. tall
   d. massive

5. In line 6, *celsae* modifies
   a. *turres* (line 7)
   b. *decidunt* (line 7)
   c. *montis* (line 8)
   d. *graviore* (line 6)

6. The case of *casu* (line 6) is determined by
   a. *graviore* (line 6)
   b. *decidunt* (line 7)
   c. *celsae* (line 6)
   d. *turres* (line 7)

7. The translation of *feriunt* (line 7) is
    a. strike
    b. bear
    c. drive wild
    d. bring

8. The case and number of *montis* (line 8) are
    a. genitive singular
    b. accusative plural
    c. ablative plural
    d. nominative plural

9. A figure of speech found in line 9 is
    a. asyndeton
    b. oxymoron
    c. personification
    d. chiasmus

10. In lines 9–11, the poet advises his listener to
    a. hope amidst favorable circumstances, fear amidst hostile ones
    b. hope and fear in moderation
    c. prepare for fate to repeat itself
    d. expect circumstances to undergo reversal

11. In line 11, *informis* modifies
    a. *Iuppiter* (line 12)
    b. *hiemes* (line 11)
    c. *reducit* (line 11)
    d. *idem* (line 12)

12. From lines 11–13, we learn that Jupiter
    a. has no visible form
    b. alters climate
    c. changes weather
    d. rules everything

Translation *Suggested time: 15 minutes*

Translate the passage below as literally as possible.

> Rectius vives, Licini, neque altum
> semper urgendo, neque—dum procellas
> cautus horrescis—nimium premendo
>   litus iniquum.
>
> aureum quisquis mediocritatem   5
> diligit, tutus caret obsoleti
> sordibus tecti, caret invidenda
>   sobrius aula.

_____

_____

_____

_____

_____

_____

_____

_____

_____

_____

Short Analysis Questions *Suggested time: 10 minutes*

. . . non, si male nunc, et olim
sic erit: quondam cithara tacentem
suscitat Musam, neque semper arcum
    tendit Apollo.

rebus angustis animosus atque   5
fortis appare: sapienter idem
contrahes vento nimium secundo
    turgida vela.

1. What contrast does the poet make with the words *non, si male nunc, et olim sic erit* (lines 1–2)? Cite and translate the Latin words that support your answer.

    _____

    _____

    _____

2. a. What actions are attributed to Apollo in lines 2–4?

    _____

    _____

  b. How do these actions reinforce the theme of this ode?

    _____

    _____

3. Explain the contrast drawn in the second stanza between two modes of action. Cite and translate or paraphrase the supporting Latin words.

    _____

    _____

    _____

4. Copy and scan line 6.

    _____

Essay *Suggested time: 20 minutes.*

saepius ventis agitatur ingens
pinus et celsae graviore casu
decidunt turres feriuntque summos
    fulgura montis.

sperat infestis, metuit secundis   5
alteram sortem bene praeparatum
pectus. informis hiemes reducit
    Iuppiter, idem

submovet. non, si male nunc, et olim
sic erit: quondam cithara tacentem   10
suscitat Musam, neque semper arcum
    tendit Apollo.

rebus angustis animosus atque
fortis appare: sapienter idem
contrahes vento nimium secundo   15
    turgida vela.

The ode from which this passage is taken has been criticized for elaborating only one point: that a person should be cautious in success and resolute in adversity. In a short, well-organized essay, discuss the techniques by which Horace in this passage tries to sustain the reader's interest as he develops this point.

Support your assertions with references to the Latin text **throughout** the passage. All Latin words must be copied or their line numbers provided, AND they must be translated or paraphrased closely enough so that it is clear you understand the Latin. It is your responsibility to convince your reader that you are basing your conclusions on the Latin text and not merely on a general recollection of the passage. Direct your answer to the question; do not merely summarize the passage. Please write your essay on a separate piece of paper.

Scansion

Scan the following lines and name the meter.

saepius ventis agitatur ingens

pinus et celsae graviore casu

decidunt turres feriuntque summos

    fulgura montis.

sperat infestis, metuit secundis   5

alteram sortem bene praeparatum

pectus. informis hiemes reducit

    Iuppiter, idem

ODE 2.14

Eheu fugaces, Postume, Postume,
labuntur anni, nec pietas moram
    rugis et instanti senectae
        adferet indomitaeque morti,

non, si trecenis, quotquot eunt dies,   5
amice, places inlacrimabilem
    Plutona tauris, qui ter amplum
        Geryonen Tityonque tristi

conpescit unda, scilicet omnibus,
quicumque terrae munere vescimur,   10
    enaviganda, sive reges,
        sive inopes erimus coloni.

frustra cruento Marte carebimus
fractisque rauci fluctibus Hadriae,
    frustra per autumnos nocentem   15
        corporibus metuemus Austrum:

visendus ater flumine languido
Cocytos errans et Danai genus
    infame damnatusque longi
        Sisyphus Aeolides laboris.   20

linquenda tellus et domus et placens
uxor, neque harum, quas colis, arborum
    te praeter invisas cupressos
        ulla brevem dominum sequetur,

absumet heres Caecuba dignior   25
servata centum clavibus et mero
    tinguet pavimentum superbo,
        pontificum potiore cenis.

Short Answer Questions

Line 1   What figure of speech (non-AP) is in this line? _____

                What does *fugaces* modify? _____

Line 3   What is the case and use of *rugis*? _____

Line 5   What figure of speech is in this line? _____

              What does *trecenis* modify?_____

Line 6   What is the case and use of *amice?*_____

              What form is *places,* and why is it used?_____

              _____

Line 7   What is the case and use of *tauris?* _____

              What does *ter* modify? _____

Line 8–9   What two figures of speech are in these lines? _____

Line 9   What two figures of speech are in this line? _____

              What is the case and use of *unda?* _____

Line 10   What figure of speech is in this line? _____

              What is the case and use of *terrae?* _____

Line 11   What is the case and use of *reges?* _____

Line 12   What is the case and use of *coloni?* _____

Line 13   What is the case and use of *Marte?* _____

Line 14   What two figures of speech are in this line? _____

              What is the case and use of *fluctibus?* _____

Line 15   What does *nocentem* modify? _____

Lines 13–16   What figure of speech is in these lines? _____

Line 17   What is the case and use of *flumine?* _____

Line 18   What is the case and use of *genus?* _____

Lines 17–18   What two figures of speech are in these lines? _____

Line 19   What does *infame* modify? _____

Lines 19–20   What figure of speech is in these lines? _____

Line 21   What figure of speech is in this line? _____

              What does *linquenda* modify?_____

Lines 21–22   What figure of speech is in these lines? _____

Line 22   What is the antecedent of *quas?* _____

              What is the case and use of *arborum?* _____

Line 23   What is the case and use of *te?*_____

Line 24   What is the case and use of *ulla?* _____

What is meant by *brevem dominum?* _____

What is the case and use of *dominum?* _____

Line 25   What is the case and use of *Caecuba?* _____

Line 26   What two figures of speech are in this line? _____

What is the case and use of *clavibus?* _____

What is the case and use of *mero?* _____

Line 27   What two figures of speech are in this line? _____

Line 28   What is the case and use of *pontificum?* _____

What does *potiore* modify? _____

What is the case and use of *cenis?* _____

Multiple Choice Questions *Suggested time: 15 minutes*

Eheu fugaces, Postume, Postume,
labuntur anni, nec pietas moram
    rugis et instanti senectae
        adferet indomitaeque morti,

non, si trecenis, quotquot eunt dies,   5
amice, places inlacrimabilem
    Plutona tauris, qui ter amplum
        Geryonen Tityonque tristi

conpescit unda, scilicet omnibus,
quicumque terrae munere vescimur,   10
    enaviganda, sive reges,
        sive inopes erimus coloni.

1. What element of tone is established in lines 1–4?
    a. irony   b. tragedy
    c. pathos   d. sarcasm

2. The words *fugaces . . . labuntur anni* (lines 1–2) are translated
    a. fugitives of the year slip away   b. you will flee, the years glide by
    c. the fleeing years labor   d. the years slide by fleeing

3. According to the words *nec . . . adferet* (lines 2–4), piety will not bring

    a. an easy death

    b. a delay of aging

    c. a regretful old age

    d. death to wrinkles and old age

4. A figure of speech contained in line 3 is

    a. hendiadys

    b. transferred epithet

    c. synecdoche

    d. chiasmus

5. The case of *morti* (line 4) is determined by

    a. *adferet* (line 4)

    b. *indomitae* (line 4)

    c. *senectae* (line 3)

    d. *moram* (line 2)

6. From lines 5–7, we learn that Pluto

    a. demands sacrifices of bulls

    b. delays death for those who sacrifice

    c. is not won over by tears

    d. is friendly to Postumus

7. In line 7, *qui* refers to

    a. *Plutona* (line 7)

    b. the subject of *places* (line 6)

    c. *tauris* (line 7)

    d. *amice* (line 6)

8. Geryon and Tityos (line 8) were

    a. friends

    b. philosophers

    c. tyrants

    d. monsters

9. In line 8, *tristi* modifies

    a. *Geryonen* (line 8)

    b. *Tityon* (line 8)

    c. *unda* (line 9)

    d. *qui* (line 7)

10. In line 9, *unda* is a reference to

    a. the sea

    b. the River Styx

    c. reflection in the water

    d. tears

11. The words *quicumque . . . vescimur* (line 10) are translated

    a. whoever feed on the gift of the earth

    b. however we perform our duty for the earth

    c. whoever we are, fed by the service of the earth

    d. whoever we are who feed on the gift of the earth

12. Lines 11–12 reinforce the point that

    a. the future is an open book

    b. death awaits all equally

    c. the simple life is the happiest

    d. life is short

Translation *Suggested time: 15 minutes*

Translate the passage below as literally as possible.

> frustra cruento Marte carebimus
> fractisque rauci fluctibus Hadriae,
>> frustra per autumnos nocentem
>>> corporibus metuemus Austrum:
>
> visendus ater flumine languido   5
> Cocytos errans et Danai genus
>> infame damnatusque longi
>>> Sisyphus Aeolides laboris.

_____

_____

_____

_____

_____

_____

_____

_____

_____

Short Analysis Questions *Suggested time: 10 minutes*

frustra cruento Marte carebimus
fractisque rauci fluctibus Hadriae,
    frustra per autumnos nocentem
      corporibus metuemus Austrum:

visendus ater flumine languido   5
Cocytos errans et Danai genus
    infame damnatusque longi
      Sisyphus Aeolides laboris.

1. Lines 1–4 say that we shall do certain things in vain (*frustra*).

   a. What are these things?

       _____

       _____

   b. Why shall our performance of them be in vain?

       _____

       _____

2. What is *Cocytos* (line 6), and why is its mention appropriate in this context?

       _____

       _____

3. Copy and scan line 7.

       _____

4. Name a figure of speech found in lines 7–8, and write out the Latin word(s) that illustrate it.

       _____

Essay *Suggested time: 20 minutes*

frustra cruento Marte carebimus
fractisque rauci fluctibus Hadriae,
    frustra per autumnos nocentem
        corporibus metuemus Austrum:

visendus ater flumine languido   5
Cocytos errans et Danai genus
    infame damnatusque longi
        Sisyphus Aeolides laboris.

linquenda tellus et domus et placens
uxor, neque harum, quas colis, arborum   10
    te praeter invisas cupressos
        ulla brevem dominum sequetur,

absumet heres Caecuba dignior
servata centum clavibus et mero
    tinguet pavimentum superbo,   15
        pontificum potiore cenis.

In the passage above, Horace develops the theme that human beings cannot escape death. In a short, well-organized essay, discuss how he uses imagery to help him develop this theme in this passage.

Support your assertions with references to the Latin text **throughout** the passage. All Latin words must be copied or their line numbers provided, AND they must be translated or paraphrased closely enough so that it is clear you understand the Latin. It is your responsibility to convince your reader that you are basing your conclusions on the Latin text and not merely on a general recollection of the passage. Direct your answer to the question; do not merely summarize the passage. Please write your essay on a separate piece of paper.

Scansion

Scan the following lines and name the meter.

> non, si trecenis, quotquot eunt dies,
>
> amice, places inlacrimabilem
>
> > Plutona tauris, qui ter amplum
> >
> > > Geryonen Tityonque tristi
>
> conpescit unda, scilicet omnibus,   5
>
> quicumque terrae munere vescimur,
>
> > enaviganda, sive reges,
> >
> > > sive inopes erimus coloni.

ODE 3.1

Odi profanum volgus et arceo.
favete linguis: carmina non prius
    audita Musarum sacerdos
       virginibus puerisque canto.

regum timendorum in proprios greges,   5
reges in ipsos imperium est Iovis,
    clari Giganteo triumpho,
       cuncta supercilio moventis.

est, ut viro vir latius ordinet
arbusta sulcis, hic generosior   10
    descendat in campum petitor,
       moribus hic meliorque fama

contendat, illi turba clientium
sit maior: aequa lege Necessitas
    sortitur insignis et imos,   15
       omne capax movet urna nomen.

destrictus ensis cui super impia
cervice pendet, non Siculae dapes
    dulcem elaborabunt saporem,
       non avium citharaeque cantus   20

somnum reducent: somnus agrestium
lenis virorum non humilis domos
    fastidit umbrosamque ripam,
       non Zephyris agitata Tempe.

desiderantem quod satis est neque   25
tumultuosum sollicitat mare,
    nec saevus Arcturi cadentis,
       impetus aut orientis Haedi,

non verberatae grandine vineae
fundusque mendax, arbore nunc aquas   30
    culpante, nunc torrentia agros
       sidera, nunc hiemes iniquas.

contracta pisces aequora sentiunt
iactis in altum molibus: huc frequens
    caementa demittit redemptor   35
        cum famulis dominusque terrae

fastidiosus, sed Timor et Minae
scandunt eodem, quo dominus, neque
    decedit aerata triremi et
        post equitem sedet atra Cura.   40

quodsi dolentem nec Phrygius lapis,
nec purpurarum sidere clarior
    delenit usus, nec Falerna
        vitis Achaemeniumque costum,

cur invidendis postibus et novo   45
sublime ritu moliar atrium?
    cur valle permutem Sabina
        divitias operosiores?

Short Answer Questions

Line 1   What is the direct object of *arceo?* _____

Line 2   What is the case and use of *carmina?*_____

Line 3   What is the case and use of *sacerdos?* _____

Line 4   What is the case and use of *virginibus puerisque?*_____

Line 5   What is the translation of *timendorum?*_____

Lines 5–6   What figure of speech is in these lines? _____
                _____

Line 7   What is the case and use of *triumpho?*_____

Line 8   What is the grammatical function of *cuncta?*_____

Line 9   What is the best translation of *est* in its context? _____

                What is the case and use of *viro?* _____

                What is the form *latius?* _____

                What figure of speech is in this line? _____

Lines 9–14   In what attribute is each of the four men described in lines 9–14 superior? _____
                _____
                _____

Line 13   What is the case and use of *turba?* _____

Line 14   What is the case and use of *lege?* _____

Line 16   What does the urn symbolize?_____

Line 17   What is the antecedent of *cui?* _____

Line 18   What is the case and use of *cervice?*_____

Line 20   What is the case and use of *avium citharaeque?*_____

Line 21   What figure of speech is in this line? _____

                 _____

Line 22   What is the case and use of *virorum?* _____

Lines 22–23   What figure of speech is in these lines? _____

Line 24   Of what is *Tempe* the object? _____

Line 26   What is the direct object of *sollicitat?* _____

Line 28   What is the case and use of *impetus?* _____

Line 29   What is the case and use of *grandine?* _____

Line 31   What is the case and use of *agros?* _____

Lines 30–32   What three figures of speech are in these lines? _____

                 _____

Line 33   What is the case and use of *pisces?* _____

                 What is the case and use of *aequora?* _____

Line 34   What is the case and use of *molibus?* _____

Lines 36–37   What two figures of speech are in these lines? _____

                 _____

Line 39   What is the subject of *decedit?*_____

                 What is the case and use of *trireme?* _____

Line 40   What is the figure of speech in this line? _____

Line 41   What is the function of *dolentem?* _____

Line 42   What is the case and use of *purpurarum?* _____

                 What is the case and use of *sidere?* _____

Line 44   What is the case and use of *vitis* and *costum?* _____

Line 45   What is the case and use of *postibus?* _____

Line 46   What is the case and use of *ritu?* _____

Lines 45–46   What two figures of speech (one non-AP) are in these lines? _____

                 _____

Multiple Choice Questions *Suggested time: 15 minutes*

destrictus ensis cui super impia
cervice pendet, non Siculae dapes
 dulcem elaborabunt saporem,
  non avium citharaeque cantus

somnum reducent: somnus agrestium   5
lenis virorum non humilis domos
 fastidit umbrosamque ripam,
  non Zephyris agitata Tempe.

desiderantem quod satis est neque
tumultuosum sollicitat mare,   10
 nec saevus Arcturi cadentis,
  impetus aut orientis Haedi, . . .

1. Lines 1–5 allude to the story of the

 a. Apple of Discord   b. Primeval Flood
 c. Pirates and Julius Caesar   d. Sword of Damocles

2. The case of *cui* (line 1) is determined by

 a. *pendet* (line 2)   b. *ensis* (line 1)
 c. *destrictus* (line 1)   d. *super* (line 1)

3. From lines 1–5, we learn that the fearful rich person

 a. is kept awake by birds singing   b. does not enjoy banquets
 c. is not virtuous   d. has lost his weapons

4. The case and number of *cantus* (line 4) are

 a. accusative plural   b. nominative plural
 c. nominative singular   d. genitive singular

5. The word closest in meaning to *citharae* (line 4) is

 a. *lyrae*   b. *tibiae*
 c. *tubae*   d. *cicadae*

6. The tense and mood of *reducent* (line 5) are

 a. present indicative   b. present subjunctive
 c. perfect indicative   d. future indicative

7. In line 6, *lenis* modifies

    a. *Zephyris* (line 8)   b. *domos* (line 6)

    c. *humilis* (line 6)   d. *somnus* (line 5)

8. A figure of speech found in lines 5–7 is

    a. personification   b. hyperbole

    c. anaphora   d. hendiadys

9. In line 8, *Zephyris* is ablative of

    a. personal agent   b. separation

    c. means   d. place where

10. In line 9, *desiderantem* modifies

    a. *tumultuosum* (line 10)   b. an understood *hominem*

    c. *satis* (line 9)   d. *mare* (line 10)

11. From lines 9–12, we learn that changes in weather do not worry the person who

    a. lives by the shady river bank   b. desires what is enough

    c. is not savage   d. stays on his farm

12. The imagery in lines 11–12 concerns

    a. seas   b. barbarian tribes

    c. stars   d. rivers

Translation *Suggested time: 15 minutes*

Translate the passage below as literally as possible.

> **est, ut viro vir latius ordinet**
> **arbusta sulcis, hic generosior**
> > **descendat in campum petitor,**
> > > **moribus hic meliorque fama**
>
> **contendat, illi turba clientium**   5
> **sit maior: aequa lege Necessitas**
> > **sortitur insignis et imos,**
> > > **omne capax movet urna nomen.**

_____

_____

_____

_____

_____

_____

_____

_____

_____

_____

Short Analysis Questions *Suggested time: 10 minutes.*

Odi profanum volgus et arceo.
favete linguis: carmina non prius
   audita Musarum sacerdos
      virginibus puerisque canto.

regum timendorum in proprios greges,   5
reges in ipsos imperium est Iovis,
   clari Giganteo triumpho,
      cuncta supercilio moventis.

1.   What are three things Horace says about himself in lines 2–4? Write out the Latin words which contain his references to each thing.

    _____

    _____

2.   What are three reasons Horace gives in lines 5–8 for us to believe in the greatness of the god Jupiter? Write out the Latin words in which Horace states each attribute of greatness.

    _____

    _____

3.   a.   Copy and scan lines 6–7.

    _____

   b.   Name the meter.

    _____

Essay *Suggested time: 20 minutes.*

contracta pisces aequora sentiunt
iactis in altum molibus: huc frequens
    caementa demittit redemptor
        cum famulis dominusque terrae

fastidiosus, sed Timor et Minae   5
scandunt eodem, quo dominus, neque
    decedit aerata triremi et
        post equitem sedet atra Cura.

quodsi dolentem nec Phrygius lapis,
nec purpurarum sidere clarior   10
    delenit usus, nec Falerna
        vitis Achaemeniumque costum,

cur invidendis postibus et novo
sublime ritu moliar atrium?
    cur valle permutem Sabina   15
        divitias operosiores?

In these lines Horace reflects on the question of how wealth contributes to happiness. In a **short,** well-organized essay, set forth your interpretation of Horace's view and show how he expresses it in the passage.

Support your assertions with references to the Latin text **throughout** the quoted passage. All Latin words must be copied or their line numbers provided, AND they must be translated or paraphrased closely enough so that it is clear you understand the Latin. It is your responsibility to convince your reader that you are basing your conclusions on the Latin text and not merely on a general recollection of the passage. Direct your answer to the question; do not merely summarize the passage. Please write your essay on a separate piece of paper.

Scansion

Scan the following lines and name the meter.

> regum timendorum in proprios greges,
>
> reges in ipsos imperium est Iovis,
>
> > clari Giganteo triumpho,
>
> > > cuncta supercilio moventis.
>
>
> est, ut viro vir latius ordinet   5
>
> arbusta sulcis, hic generosior
>
> > descendat in campum petitor,
>
> > > moribus hic meliorque fama

ODE 3.9

Donec gratus eram tibi,
    nec quisquam potior brachia candidae
cervici iuvenis dabat,
    Persarum vigui rege beatior.

'donec non alia magis   5
    arsisti, neque erat Lydia post Chloen,
multi Lydia nominis
    Romana vigui clarior Ilia.'

me nunc Thressa Chloe regit,
    dulcis docta modos et citharae sciens,   10
pro qua non metuam mori,
    si parcent animae fata superstiti.

'me torret face mutua
    Thurini Calais filius Ornyti,
pro quo bis patiar mori,   15
    si parcent puero fata superstiti.'

quid si prisca redit Venus
    diductosque iugo cogit aeneo,
si flava excutitur Chloe,
    reiectaeque patet ianua Lydiae?   20

'quamquam sidere pulchrior
    ille est, tu levior cortice et inprobo
iracundior Hadria,
    tecum vivere amem, tecum obeam libens.'

Short Answer Questions

Line 1   What is the case and use of *tibi?* _____

Line 2   What is the function of *quisquam?* _____

                 What is the case and use of *brachia?* _____

Line 3   What is the case and use of *cervici?* _____

Line 4   What is the case and use of *rege?* _____

Line 6   What figure of speech is in this line? _____

Line 9   What is the case and use of *me*? _____

Line 10   What figure of speech is in this line? _____

Line 12   What is the case and use of *fata*? _____

Line 13   What is the case and use of *face*? _____

               What figure of speech is in this line? _____

Line 14   What figure of speech is in this line? _____

Lines 15–16   What figure of speech is in these lines? _____

Line 17   What figure of speech is in this line? _____

Line 18   What is the case and use of *diductos*? _____

               What figure of speech is in this line? _____

Line 21   What is the case and use of *sidere*? _____

Line 22   What three figures of speech are in this line? _____

               _____

               What is the case and use of *cortice*? _____

Line 24   What two figures of speech are in this line? _____

               _____

Multiple Choice Questions *Suggested time: 15 minutes*

'donec non alia magis
  arsisti, neque erat Lydia post Chloen,
multi Lydia nominis
  Romana vigui clarior Ilia.'

me nunc Thressa Chloe regit,   5
  dulcis docta modos et citharae sciens,
pro qua non metuam mori,
  si parcent animae fata superstiti.

'me torret face mutua
  Thurini Calais filius Ornyti,   10
pro quo bis patiar mori,
  si parcent puero fata superstiti.'

1. A figure of speech found in lines 1–2 is
   a. asyndeton
   c. metonymy
   b. tmesis
   d. enjambment

2. The case and number of *alia* (line 1) are
   a. nominative plural
   c. ablative singular
   b. nominative singular
   d. accusative plural

3. The best translation of *donec* (line 1) is
   a. as long as
   c. until
   b. and I do not give
   d. gift

4. In line 3, *multi . . .* refers to
   a. many names
   c. many famous people
   b. being well known
   d. a long line of ancestors

5. From lines 1–4, we learn that in the past, Lydia was
   a. much talked about
   c. burning with love
   b. second to Chloe
   d. also called Ilia

6. In line 5, *me* refers to
   a. Lydia
   c. the Thracian woman
   b. Chloe
   d. Lydia's lover

7. The case and number of *modos* (line 6) are determined by
    a. *docta* (line 6)
    b. *dulcis* (line 6)
    c. *sciens* (line 6)
    d. *regit* (line 5)

8. The antecedent of *qua* (line 7) is
    a. *cithara* (line 6)
    b. *Chloe* (line 5)
    c. *docta* (line 6)
    d. *me* (line 5)

9. Line 8, *si . . . superstiti,* is translated
    a. if the survivors spare the soul's fate
    b. if the souls spare the fates of the survivor
    c. if they spare the surviving fates of her life
    d. if the fates spare her life surviving

10. The form *mori* (line 7) is
    a. genitive singular
    b. imperative singular
    c. present infinitive
    d. nominative plural

11. The speaker of lines 9–12 says that her love for her beloved is
    a. unrequited
    b. eternal
    c. undeserved
    d. returned equally

12. The best translation of *patiar* (line 11) is
    a. I will endure
    b. let me suffer
    c. I am allowed
    d. I will be allowed

13. A figure of speech found in line 11 is
    a. asyndeton
    b. hysteron proteron
    c. hyperbole
    d. ellipsis

14. In line 12, *puero* denotes the same person as
    a. *me* (line 9)
    b. *filius* (line 10)
    c. *Ornyti* (line 10)
    d. the subject of *patiar* (line 11)

Translation *Suggested time: 15 minutes*

Translate the passage below as literally as possible.

> quid si prisca redit Venus
>   diductosque iugo cogit aeneo,
> si flava excutitur Chloe,
>   reiectaeque patet ianua Lydiae?
>
> 'quamquam sidere pulchrior   5
>   ille est, tu levior cortice et inprobo
> iracundior Hadria,
>   tecum vivere amem, tecum obeam libens.'

_____

_____

_____

_____

_____

_____

_____

_____

_____

_____

Short Analysis Questions *Suggested time: 10 minutes*

> Donec gratus eram tibi,
>   nec quisquam potior brachia candidae
> cervici iuvenis dabat,
>   Persarum vigui rege beatior.

1. What do the adjectives in this passage suggest about the feelings that the speaker had during the time about which he is speaking now? Refer specifically to four Latin adjectives.

    _____

    _____

    _____

2. Name a figure of speech that occurs in line 4. Write out the Latin words that illustrate it.

_____

_____

Essay *Suggested time: 20 minutes*

Donec gratus eram tibi,
    nec quisquam potior brachia candidae
cervici iuvenis dabat,
    Persarum vigui rege beatior.

'donec non alia magis   5
    arsisti, neque erat Lydia post Chloen,
multi Lydia nominis
    Romana vigui clarior Ilia.'

me nunc Thressa Chloe regit,
    dulcis docta modos et citharae sciens,   10
pro qua non metuam mori,
    si parcent animae fata superstiti.

'me torret face mutua
    Thurini Calais filius Ornyti,
pro quo bis patiar mori,   15
    si parcent puero fata superstiti.'

quid si prisca redit Venus
    diductosque iugo cogit aeneo,
si flava excutitur Chloe,
    reiectaeque patet ianua Lydiae?   20

'quamquam sidere pulchrior
    ille est, tu levior cortice et inprobo
iracundior Hadria,
    tecum vivere amem, tecum obeam libens.'

In this ode, Horace uses time as a structuring element of the lovers' conversation about their relationship. In a **short,** well-organized essay, discuss how their reflection on the past and present influences the lovers' feelings about a future together.

Support your assertions with references to the Latin text **throughout** the poem. All Latin words must be copied or their line numbers provided, AND they must be translated or paraphrased closely enough so that it is clear you understand the Latin. It is your responsibility to convince your reader that you are basing your conclusions on the Latin text and not merely on a general recollection of the passage. Direct your answer to the question; do not merely summarize the passage. Please write your essay on a separate piece of paper.

Scansion

Scan the following lines and name the meter.

Donec gratus eram tibi,

    nec quisquam potior brachia candidae

cervici iuvenis dabat,

    Persarum vigui rege beatior.

'donec non alia magis   5

    arsisti, neque erat Lydia post Chloen,

multi Lydia nominis

    Romana vigui clarior Ilia.'

ODE 3.13

O fons Bandusiae splendidior vitro,
dulci digne mero non sine floribus,
   cras donaberis haedo,
      cui frons turgida cornibus

primis et Venerem et proelia destinat,   5
frustra: nam gelidos inficiet tibi
   rubro sanguine rivos
      lascivi suboles gregis.

te flagrantis atrox hora Caniculae
nescit tangere, tu frigus amabile   10
   fessis vomere tauris
      praebes et pecori vago.

fies nobilium tu quoque fontium
me dicente cavis inpositam ilicem
   saxis, unde loquaces   15
      lymphae desiliunt tuae.

Short Answer Questions

Line 1   What is the case and use of *fons?* _____

                What is the case and use of *vitro?* _____

Line 2   What figure of speech is in this line? _____

Line 3   What is the case and use of *haedo?* _____

Line 4   What is the antecedent of *cui?* _____

                What is the case and use of *cornibus?* _____

Line 5   What two figures of speech are in this line? _____

Line 6   What is the subject of *inficiet?* _____

                What is the case and use of *tibi?* _____

Line 7   What is the case and use of *sanguine?* _____

Lines 6–7   How does the word order of *gelidos . . . rivos* help to create an image? _____
                   _____

Line 8   What is the case and use of *lascivi*? _____

Line 9   What is the case and use of *te*? _____

Line 11   What is the case and use of *vomere*? _____

Line 12   What is the case and use of *pecori*? _____

Line 13   What is the translation of *fies*? _____

Lines 14–15   What two figures of speech (one non-AP) are in these lines? _____
              _____

Multiple Choice Questions *Suggested time: 15 minutes*

**te flagrantis atrox hora Caniculae
nescit tangere, tu frigus amabile
    fessis vomere tauris
        praebes et pecori vago.**

fies nobilium tu quoque fontium   5
**me dicente cavis inpositam ilicem
    saxis, unde loquaces
        lymphae desiliunt tuae.**

1. From lines 1–2, we learn that the Bandusian spring
    a. grows warmer at the savage season   b. is avoided by fierce dogs
    c. does not know to touch the blazing hour   d. is not affected in summer

2. *Caniculae* (line 1) refers to a
    a. nymph   b. star
    c. village   d. brook

3. The case of *frigus* (line 2) is determined by
    a. *vomere* (line 3)   b. *amabile* (line 2)
    c. *fessis* (line 3)   d. *praebes* (line 4)

4. The *tauris* referred to in line 3
    a. carry water   b. pull the plow
    c. protect the herd   d. fight love battles

5. The subject of *praebes* (line 4) is
    a. the spring   b. the reader
    c. Canicula   d. the herdsman

6. The case and number of *pecori* (line 4) are

    a. genitive singular

    c. ablative singular

    b. nominative plural

    d. dative singular

7. The tense and mood of *fies* (line 5) are

    a. present indicative

    c. future indicative

    b. present subjunctive

    d. imperfect subjunctive

8. In lines 5–6, the poet pledges to

    a. make the spring famous

    c. sacrifice a kid

    b. plant a tree at the spring

    d. draw inspiration from the spring

9. The case of *saxis* (line 7) is determined by

    a. *cavis* (line 6)

    c. *ilicem* (line 6)

    b. *inpositam* (line 6)

    d. *dicente* (line 6)

10. In line 7, *loquaces* modifies

    a. *tuae* (line 8)

    c. *lymphae* (line 8)

    b. *desiliunt* (line 8)

    d. *unde* (line 7)

11. From lines 6–8, we learn that the spring

    a. stands above an ilex tree

    c. proceeds from hollow rocks

    b. leaps out from a hollow tree

    d. flows quietly

12. A figure of speech found in lines 7–8 is

    a. alliteration

    c. oxymoron

    b. transferred epithet

    d. hyperbaton

Translation *Suggested time: 15 minutes.*

Translate the passage below as literally as possible.

> **O fons Bandusiae splendidior vitro,**
> **dulci digne mero non sine floribus,**
> **cras donaberis haedo,**
> **cui frons turgida cornibus**
>
> **primis et Venerem et proelia destinat,**
> **frustra: nam gelidos inficiet tibi**
> **rubro sanguine rivos**
> **lascivi suboles gregis.**

5

_____

_____

_____

_____

_____

_____

_____

_____

_____

_____

Short Analysis Questions *Suggested time: 10 minutes.*

te flagrantis atrox hora Caniculae
nescit tangere, tu frigus amabile
    fessis vomere tauris
      praebes et pecori vago.

fies nobilium tu quoque fontium   5
me dicente cavis inpositam ilicem
    saxis, unde loquaces
      lymphae desiliunt tuae.

1.   Name a figure of speech in lines 1–2 and write out the Latin words that illustrate it.

        _____

2.   In lines 1–2,

    a. explain what *Caniculae* is.

          _____

    b. identify and translate *atrox hora Caniculae*.

          _____

    c. explain the significance of *te . . . nescit tangere* in this context.

          _____

3.   Name two beneficiaries of the spring's action in lines 2–4 and translate the supporting Latin.

_____

_____

_____

Essay _Suggested time: 20 minutes_

O fons Bandusiae splendidior vitro,
dulci digne mero non sine floribus,
   cras donaberis haedo,
      cui frons turgida cornibus

primis et Venerem et proelia destinat,   5
frustra: nam gelidos inficiet tibi
   rubro sanguine rivos
      lascivi suboles gregis.

te flagrantis atrox hora Caniculae
nescit tangere, tu frigus amabile   10
   fessis vomere tauris
      praebes et pecori vago.

fies nobilium tu quoque fontium
me dicente cavis inpositam ilicem
   saxis, unde loquaces   15
      lymphae desiliunt tuae.

One of the features that make Horace's poetry so memorable is its juxtaposition of contrasting qualities or expectations. In a brief, well-organized essay, show how Horace exploits contrasts to enhance the effect of the poem.

Support your assertions with references to the Latin text **throughout** the poem. All Latin words must be copied or their line numbers provided, AND they must be translated or paraphrased closely enough so that it is clear you understand the Latin. It is your responsibility to convince your reader that you are basing your conclusions on the Latin text and not merely on a general recollection of the passage. Direct your answer to the question; do not merely summarize the passage. Please write your essay on a separate piece of paper.

Scansion

Scan the following lines and name the meter.

te flagrantis atrox hora Caniculae

nescit tangere, tu frigus amabile

fessis vomere tauris

praebes et pecori vago.

fies nobilium tu quoque fontium   5

me dicente cavis inpositam ilicem

saxis, unde loquaces

lymphae desiliunt tuae.

ODE 3.30

Exegi monumentum aere perennius
regalique situ pyramidum altius,

quod non imber edax, non Aquilo inpotens
possit diruere aut innumerabilis

annorum series et fuga temporum.   5
non omnis moriar, multaque pars mei

vitabit Libitinam: usque ego postera
crescam laude recens, dum Capitolium

scandet cum tacita virgine pontifex.
dicar, qua violens obstrepit Aufidus   10

et qua pauper aquae Daunus agrestium
regnavit populorum, ex humili potens

princeps Aeolium carmen ad Italos
deduxisse modos. sume superbiam

quaesitam meritis et mihi Delphica   15
lauro cinge volens, Melpomene, comam.

Short Answer Questions

Line 1   What is the case and use of *aere?* _____

              What does *perennius* modify? _____

Line 2   What is the case and use of *situ?* _____

              What is the case and use of *pyramidum?* _____

Line 3   What is the antecedent of *quod?* _____

              Name three figures of speech in this line. _____

Line 4   What is (are) the subject(s) of *possit?* _____

Line 5   What two figures of speech are in this line? _____

              What is the case and use of *temporum?* _____

Lines 3–5   What figure of speech is in these lines? _____

Line 8   What is the case and use of *laude?* _____

Line 9   What is the case and use of *virgine?* _____

Line 11   What is the case and use of *aquae?* _____

Line 12   What is the case and use of *populorum?* _____

Line 13   What is the case and use of *carmen?* _____

Line 14   On what verb does *deduxisse* depend? _____

Lines 13–14   What three figures of speech are in these lines? _____
_____

Line 15   What is the case and use of *mihi?* _____

Line 16   What is the case and use of *lauro?* _____

What is the case and use of *comam?* _____

Multiple Choice Questions *Suggested time: 15 minutes*

**Exegi monumentum aere perennius
regalique situ pyramidum altius,**

**quod non imber edax, non Aquilo inpotens
possit diruere aut innumerabilis**

**annorum series et fuga temporum.   5
non omnis moriar, multaque pars mei**

**vitabit Libitinam: usque ego postera
crescam laude recens, dum Capitolium**

**scandet cum tacita virgine pontifex.   10
dicar, qua violens obstrepit Aufidus**

**et qua pauper aquae Daunus agrestium
regnavit populorum, . . .**

1.   The *monumentum* that Horace describes in lines 1–5 is
   a.   a building   b.   a statue
   c.   poetry   d.   a farm

2. In line 1, *exegi* is translated
    a. I have completed
    b. I have driven out
    c. I have exacted
    d. I have reduced

3. The case of *regali* (line 2) is determined by
    a. *situ* (line 2)
    b. *exegi* (line 1)
    c. *aere* (line 1)
    d. *perennius* (line 1)

4. In line 2, *altius* modifies
    a. *perennius* (line 1)
    b. *situ* (line 2)
    c. *exegi* (line 1)
    d. *monumentum* (line 1)

5. A figure of speech found in line 3 is
    a. oxymoron
    b. personification
    c. hendiadys
    d. litotes

6. The word *diruere* (line 4) is
    a. present passive indicative
    b. present active infinitive
    c. present active imperative
    d. perfect active indicative

7. The characteristic that Horace does **not** attribute to the pyramids in lines 2–4 is
    a. height
    b. sacredness
    c. fame
    d. royal origin

8. From the words *non omnis . . . Libitinam* (lines 6–7), we learn that Horace believes that
    a. not everyone will die
    b. he will not delay on earth
    c. part of him will survive his death
    d. he will not die

9. The case and number of *postera* (line 7) are
    a. accusative plural
    b. nominative singular
    c. nominative plural
    d. ablative singular

10. The words *dum . . . pontifex* (lines 8–9) refer to a
    a. religious ceremony
    b. wedding procession
    c. poetic contest
    d. senatorial assembly

11. In line 10, *qua* is translated
    a. by which
    b. insofar as
    c. which
    d. where

12. From lines 10–12, we learn that Horace will be spoken of
    a. as a violent man
    b. by rural people
    c. by Daunus
    d. as living in a dry countryside

Translation *Suggested time: 15 minutes*

Translate the passage below as literally as possible.

> Exegi monumentum aere perennius
> regalique situ pyramidum altius,
>
> quod non imber edax, non Aquilo inpotens
> possit diruere aut innumerabilis
>
> annorum series et fuga temporum.   5
> non omnis moriar, multaque pars mei
>
> vitabit Libitinam: . . . .

_____

_____

_____

_____

_____

_____

_____

_____

_____

_____

_____

Short Analysis Questions *Suggested time: 10 minutes*

dicar, qua violens obstrepit Aufidus

et qua pauper aquae Daunus agrestium
regnavit populorum, ex humili potens

princeps Aeolium carmen ad Italos
deduxisse modos. sume superbiam   5

quaesitam meritis et mihi Delphica
lauro cinge volens, Melpomene, comam.

1. a. To what part of Italy does Horace refer in lines 1–3?

    _____

    b. What is the significance of his references to this part of Italy?

    _____

2. To what poetic accomplishment does Horace refer with the words *ex humili . . . modos* (lines 3–5)? Write out and translate the Latin support for your conclusion.

    _____

    _____

3. a. Who is Melpomene?

    _____

    b. What are two things she is asked to do (lines 5–7)? Cite the Latin support for each.

    _____

    _____

Essay *Suggested time: 20 minutes*

Exegi monumentum aere perennius
regalique situ pyramidum altius,

quod non imber edax, non Aquilo inpotens
possit diruere aut innumerabilis

annorum series et fuga temporum.   5
non omnis moriar, multaque pars mei

vitabit Libitinam: usque ego postera
crescam laude recens, dum Capitolium

scandet cum tacita virgine pontifex.
dicar, qua violens obstrepit Aufidus   10

et qua pauper aquae Daunus agrestium
regnavit populorum, ex humili potens

princeps Aeolium carmen ad Italos
deduxisse modos. sume superbiam

quaesitam meritis et mihi Delphica   15
lauro cinge volens, Melpomene, comam.

In this ode, Horace reflects on his finished three books of *Odes*. In a brief, well-organized essay, show how Horace uses references to time to talk about his poetic accomplishments. You may discuss, but are not limited to, verb tenses, imagery, or mythological and historical references.

Support your assertions with references to the Latin text **throughout** the poem. All Latin words must be copied or their line numbers provided, AND they must be translated or paraphrased closely enough so that it is clear you understand the Latin. It is your responsibility to convince your reader that you are basing your conclusions on the Latin text and not merely on a general recollection of the passage. Direct your answer to the question; do not merely summarize the passage. Please write your essay on a separate piece of paper.

Scansion

Scan the following lines and name the meter.

Exegi monumentum aere perennius

regalique situ pyramidum altius,

quod non imber edax, non Aquilo inpotens

possit diruere aut innumerabilis

annorum series et fuga temporum.   5

non omnis moriar, multaque pars mei

vitabit Libitinam: usque ego postera

crescam laude recens, dum Capitolium

ODE 4.7

Diffugere nives, redeunt iam gramina campis
    arboribusque comae,
mutat terra vices et decrescentia ripas
    flumina praetereunt,

Gratia cum Nymphis geminisque sororibus audet   5
    ducere nuda choros.
immortalia ne speres, monet annus et almum
    quae rapit hora diem.

frigora mitescunt Zephyris, ver proterit aestas
    interitura, simul   10
pomifer autumnus fruges effuderit, et mox
    bruma recurrit iners.

damna tamen celeres reparant caelestia lunae:
    nos ubi decidimus,
quo pater Aeneas, quo Tullus dives et Ancus,   15
    pulvis et umbra sumus.

quis scit, an adiciant hodiernae crastina summae
    tempora di superi?
cuncta manus avidas fugient heredis, amico
    quae dederis animo.   20

cum semel occideris, et de te splendida Minos
    fecerit arbitria,
non, Torquate, genus, non te facundia, non te
    restituet pietas:

infernis neque enim tenebris Diana pudicum   25
    liberat Hippolytum,
nec Lethaea valet Theseus abrumpere caro
    vincula Pirithoo.

Short Answer Questions

Line 1   What is the case and use of *campis?*_____

               The verb *diffugere* is an alternative form of what verb?_____

Lines 1–2   What three figures of speech are in these lines? _____

_____

Line 3   What is the case and use of *vices?* _____

             What is the case and use of *ripas?* _____

Line 4   What is the case and use of *flumina?* _____

Line 5   What is the case and use of *sororibus?* _____

Line 6   What figure of speech is in this line? _____

Line 7   What is the case and use of *immortalia?* _____

             What figure of speech is in this line? _____

Lines 7–8   What four figures of speech are in these lines? _____

_____

Line 9   What is the case and use of *Zephyris?* _____

             What is the case and use of *ver?* _____

Lines 9–10   What figure of speech is in these lines? _____

Line 11   What is the tense of *effuderit?* _____

             What is the case and use of *fruges?* _____

Line 12   What two figures of speech are in this line? _____

Line 13   What is the case and use of *damna?* _____

             What is the case and use of *celeres?* _____

             What is the figure of speech in this line? _____

Line 14   What figure of speech (non-AP) is in this line? _____

Line 15   What figure of speech is in this line? _____

Line 17   What is the case and use of *summae?* _____

Line 18   What is the case and use of *tempora?* _____

Line 19   What is the case and use of *cuncta?* _____

             What three figures of speech are in this line? _____

Line 20   What is the tense of *dederis?* _____

Lines 23–24   What five figures of speech are in these lines? _____

_____

Line 25   What is the case and use of *tenebris?* _____

Line 27   What is the object of *abrumpere?* _____

Multiple Choice Questions *Suggested time: 15 minutes*

Diffugere nives, redeunt iam gramina campis
    arboribusque comae,
mutat terra vices et decrescentia ripas
    flumina praetereunt,

Gratia cum Nymphis geminisque sororibus audet   5
    ducere nuda choros.
immortalia ne speres, monet annus et almum
    quae rapit hora diem.

frigora mitescunt Zephyris, ver proterit aestas
    interitura, simul   10
pomifer autumnus fruges effuderit, et mox
    bruma recurrit iners.

1. In line 1, *diffugere* is
   a. present active infinitive
   c. present passive imperative
   b. perfect active indicative
   d. future passive indicative

2. The case of *campis* (line 1) is determined by
   a. *gramina* (line 1)
   c. *iam* (line 1)
   b. *arboribus* (line 2)
   d. *redeunt* (line 1)

3. The words *decrescentia ripas flumina praetereunt* (lines 3–4) are translated
   a. cresting rivers pass beyond their banks
   c. decreasing rivers go past their banks
   b. crested banks surround rivers
   d. rivers pass by, diminishing their banks

4. From lines 1–4, we may infer that the poem is set in
   a. late winter
   c. late spring
   b. early spring
   d. summer

5. The *geminis sororibus* (line 5) are
   a. Fates
   c. Castor and Pollux
   b. Nymphs
   d. Graces

6. A figure of speech found in lines 5–6 is
   a. asyndeton
   c. prolepsis
   b. hysteron proteron
   d. hyperbaton

7. In line 7, *almum* modifies
   a. *diem* (line 8)
   b. *rapit* (line 8)
   c. *monet* (line 7)
   d. *quae* (line 8)

8. The antecedent of *quae* (line 8) is
   a. *annus* (line 7)
   b. *almum* (line 7)
   c. *immortalia* (line 7)
   d. *hora* (line 8)

9. In line 7, *ne* introduces a (an)
   a. purpose clause
   b. conditional clause
   c. indirect command
   d. result clause

10. In line 9, *Zephyris* are
    a. horses
    b. winds
    c. nymphs
    d. seasons

11. In line 10, *simul* is translated
    a. at the same time
    b. once for all
    c. simultaneously
    d. as soon as

12. In line 11, *effuderit* is
    a. future perfect indicative
    b. perfect subjunctive
    c. present indicative
    d. future indicative

13. Lines 9–12 emphasize the _____ of the seasons' change.
    a. inevitability
    b. mildness
    c. rapidity
    d. harmony

Translation *Suggested time: 15 minutes*

Translate the passage below as literally as possible.

> cum semel occideris, et de te splendida Minos
>   fecerit arbitria,
> non, Torquate, genus, non te facundia, non te
>   restituet pietas:
>
> infernis neque enim tenebris Diana pudicum
>   liberat Hippolytum,
> nec Lethaea valet Theseus abrumpere caro
>   vincula Pirithoo.

_____

_____

_____

_____

_____

_____

_____

_____

_____

_____

Short Analysis Questions *Suggested time: 10 minutes*

damna tamen celeres reparant caelestia lunae:
    nos ubi decidimus,
quo pater Aeneas, quo Tullus dives et Ancus,
    pulvis et umbra sumus.

quis scit, an adiciant hodiernae crastina summae   5
    tempora di superi?
cuncta manus avidas fugient heredis, amico
    quae dederis animo.

1.   a.   What are the losses (*damna*) of which Horace speaks in line 1?

      _____

      _____

     b.   How are these losses repaired?

      _____

      _____

2.   a.   To what place does Horace refer by the word *quo* (line 3)?

      _____

     b.   Copy and translate two pieces of evidence from the Latin that support your answer.

      _____

3.   Identify a figure of speech that appears in lines 5–6, and copy the Latin words that illustrate it.

      _____

4.   a.   According to lines 7–8, what action will prevent an heir from coming into possession of certain parts of one's wealth?

      _____

     b.   Copy and translate the Latin words that support your answer.

      _____

Essay *Suggested time: 20 minutes*

Diffugere nives, redeunt iam gramina campis
    arboribusque comae,
mutat terra vices et decrescentia ripas
    flumina praetereunt,

Gratia cum Nymphis geminisque sororibus audet   **5**
    ducere nuda choros.
immortalia ne speres, monet annus et almum
    quae rapit hora diem.

frigora mitescunt Zephyris, ver proterit aestas
    interitura, simul   **10**
pomifer autumnus fruges effuderit, et mox
    bruma recurrit iners.

damna tamen celeres reparant caelestia lunae:
    nos ubi decidimus,
quo pater Aeneas, quo Tullus dives et Ancus,   **15**
    pulvis et umbra sumus.

quis scit, an adiciant hodiernae crastina summae
    tempora di superi?
cuncta manus avidas fugient heredis, amico
    quae dederis animo.   **20**

cum semel occideris, et de te splendida Minos
    fecerit arbitria,
non, Torquate, genus, non te facundia, non te
    restituet pietas:

infernis neque enim tenebris Diana pudicum   **25**
    liberat Hippolytum,
nec Lethaea valet Theseus abrumpere caro
    vincula Pirithoo.

Horace's imagery in this ode depicts two kinds of change: change that renews itself and change that reaches an end and stops. In a **short,** well-organized essay, discuss how Horace's images of cyclical change and irreversible change help him to comment on the human condition.

Support your assertions with Latin references from **throughout** the poem. All Latin words must be copied or their line numbers provided, AND they must be translated or paraphrased closely enough so that it is clear you understand the Latin. It is your responsibility to convince your reader that you are basing your conclusions on the Latin text and not merely on a general recollection of the passage. Direct your answer to the question; do not merely summarize the passage. Please write your essay on a separate piece of paper.

Scansion

Scan the following lines and name the meter.

Diffugere nives, redeunt iam gramina campis

arboribusque comae,

mutat terra vices et decrescentia ripas

flumina praetereunt, . . .

APPENDIX

PRACTICE MULTIPLE CHOICE EXERCISES AND ANSWER KEY

PASSAGE A

Suggested time: 15 minutes per excerpt

Cicero describes the Fabricii brothers.

C. et L. Fabricii fratres gemini fuerunt ex municipio Aletrinati, homines inter
se cum forma tum moribus similes, municipum autem suorum dissimillimi,
in quibus quantus splendor sit, quam prope aequabilis, quam constans et moderata
ratio vitae, nemo vestrum, ut mea fert opinio, ignorat. His Fabriciis semper est usus
Oppianicus familiarissime. Iam hoc fere scitis omnes, quantam vim habeat ad   5
coniungendas amicitias studiorum ac naturae similitudo. Cum illi ita viverent ut
nullum quaestum esse turpem arbitrarentur, cum omnis ab eis fraus, omnes insidiae
circumscriptionesque adulescentium nascerentur, cumque essent vitiis atque
improbitate omnibus noti, studiose, ut dixi, ad eorum familiaritatem multis iam
ante annis Oppianicus se applicarat.   10

municipium, -i, n., *municipality, town*
cum . . . tum, *both. . . . and*
Aletrinas, m./f., of **Aletrium,** *a town c.50 miles southeast of Rome*
municeps, -ipis, m., *fellow townsman*
aequabilis, -e, *consistent*
Oppianicus, *the name of a citizen of another town*
studium, -i, n., *interest, pursuit*
quaestus, -us, m., *profit*
arbitror, -ari, -atus sum, *think, deem, suppose*
turpis, -e, *base, disgraceful*
circumscriptio, -ionis, f., *cheating, swindling*
vitium, -i, n., *vice, crime*
improbitas, -tatis, f., *dishonesty*
studiose, *earnestly, carefully*

1. From lines 1–2, we learn that the Fabricii brothers had similar
   a. occupations
   b. characters
   c. houses
   d. deaths

2. In line 3, *sit* is subjunctive because it appears in a clause of
   a. purpose
   b. result
   c. indirect command
   d. indirect question

3. The best translation of *ratio vitae* (line 4) is

   a. manner of life
   b. ratio of living
   c. rations for life
   d. reasonable life

4. The case and number of *vestrum* (line 4) are

   a. accusative singular
   b. nominative singular
   c. genitive plural
   d. vocative singular

5. The case of *Fabriciis* (line 4) is determined by

   a. *His* (line 4)
   b. *est usus* (line 4)
   c. *Oppianicus* (line 5)
   d. *familiarissime* (line 5)

6. In lines 5–6, everyone is said to know how

   a. friendship contributes to human nature
   b. friendship creates similar interests
   c. nature affects friendship more than interests do
   d. similar qualities help form friendships

7. In line 6, *illi* refers to

   a. an understood "you"
   b. Oppianicus
   c. the Fabricii brothers
   d. interests

8. In lines 6–8, Cicero says that the Fabricii brothers

   a. think monetary profit a disgraceful motive
   b. were the victims of fraud
   c. lived in disgrace
   d. cheated many people

9. In line 9, *improbitate* is ablative of

   a. cause
   b. manner
   c. means
   d. description

10. The tense and mood of *applicarat* (line 10) are

    a. present subjunctive
    b. imperfect subjunctive
    c. present indicative
    d. pluperfect indicative

11. From lines 9–10, we learn that Oppianicus

    a. worked for a long time to cultivate the friendship of the Fabricii
    b. tried for many years to avoid the Fabricii
    c. was long known to all for his dishonesty
    d. had long since become a member of the Fabricii family

12. Cicero's attitude toward the Fabricii brothers is one of

    a. respect
    b. disapproval
    c. indifference
    d. admiration

PASSAGE B

The hero Peleus finds the goddess Thetis on the seashore.

Est sinus Haemoniae curvos falcatus in arcus:
bracchia procurrunt, ubi, si foret altior unda,
portus erat (summis inductum est aequor harenis);
litus habet solidum, quod nec vestigia servet
nec remoretur iter, nec opertum pendeat alga.   5
Myrtea silva subest bicoloribus obsita bacis
et specus in medio (natura factus an arte,
ambiguum, magis arte tamen), quo saepe venire
frenato delphine sedens, Theti, nuda solebas.
Illic te Peleus, ut somno vincta iacebas,   10
occupat: et quoniam precibus temptata repugnas,
vim parat innectens ambobus colla lacertis.

Haemonia, -ae, f. *Thessaly* (a region of northern Greece)
falcatus, -a, -um, *curved, sickle-shaped*
remoror, -ari, -atus sum, *to detain, hinder*
operio, -ire, -ii, *opertusm, to cover*
alga, -ae, f. *seaweed*
myrteus, -a, -um, *of myrtle bushes*
obsitus, -a, -um, *overgrown, covered*
baca, -ae, f. *berry*
specus, -us, m. *cave*
freno, -are, -avi, -atum, *to bridle, curb*
repugno, -are, -avi, -atum, *to fight back against, oppose*
innecto, -ere, -nexui, -nexum, *to entwine*
collum, -i, n. *neck*
lacertus, -i, m. *arm*

1. From lines 1–2, we learn that

    a. Thetis wore a billowing hunting dress

    b. Thetis' arms extended from her flowing garment

    c. the beach was suitable for archery practice

    d. the shoreline formed a bay

2. The meaning of the words *si foret altior unda, portus erat* (lines 2–3) is

    a. if the water were deeper, there would be a port

    b. if the waves were higher, there would be a port

    c. if the wave would be deeper, there was a port

    d. if the water were higher, there was a port

3. Lines 4–5 tell us that
   a. soft sand covers the beach
   b. Thetis' footsteps remain in the sand
   c. it is easy to walk on the shore
   d. the footing does not serve the pedestrian

4. In line 5, *remoretur* is subjunctive in a(n)
   a. relative clause of characteristic
   b. indirect question
   c. relative clause of purpose
   d. jussive clause

5. In line 5, *opertum* describes
   a. *pendeat* (line 5)
   b. *litus* (line 4)
   c. *solidum* (line 4)
   d. *iter* (line 5)

6. Lines 6–8 suggest that people may have
   a. fashioned a cave in the rock
   b. planted myrtle to mark the cave
   c. painted the cave's walls
   d. harvested berries

7. A figure of speech that appears in lines 7–8 is
   a. chiasmus
   b. hendiadys
   c. synecdoche
   d. ellipsis

8. The speaker of the words *Theti, nuda solebas* (line 9) is
   a. Thetis
   b. Peleus
   c. the poet
   d. the dolphin

9. In line 10, *vincta* is a form of
   a. *vivo*
   b. *vinco*
   c. *vincio*
   d. *viso*

10. When Peleus saw Thetis, Thetis was
    a. riding on a dolphin
    b. sitting on the shore
    c. taking the bridle off the dolphin
    d. sleeping on the shore

11. The case and number of *colla* (line 12) are
    a. nominative singular
    b. nominative plural
    c. accusative plural
    d. ablative singular

12. The case of *lacertis* (line 12) is determined by
    a. *ambobus* (line 12)
    b. *innectens* (line 12)
    c. *colla* (line 12)
    d. *parat* (line 12)

13. The metrical pattern of the first four feet of line 7 (*et specus . . . .*) is
    a. dactyl-dactyl-spondee-spondee
    b. spondee-spondee-dactyl-dactyl
    c. dactyl-spondee-spondee-spondee
    d. dactyl-dactyl-spondee-dactyl

PASSAGE C

The Trojans journey over the sea.

Postquam altum tenuere rates nec iam amplius ullae
apparent terrae, caelum undique et undique pontus,
tum mihi caeruleus supra caput astitit imber
noctem hiememque ferens, et inhorruit unda tenebris.
continuo venti volvunt mare magnaque surgunt   5
aequora, dispersi iactamur gurgite vasto;
involvere diem nimbi et nox umida caelum
abstulit, ingeminant abruptis nubibus ignes.
excutimur cursu et caecis erramus in undis.
ipse diem noctemque negat discernere caelo   10
nec meminisse viae media Palinurus in unda.

caeruleus, -a, -um, *dark blue*
asto, -are, astiti, *to stand nearby*
continuo, *immediately*
involvo, -ere, involvi, involutum, *to envelop*
excutio, -ere, excussi, excussum, *to shake out, throw off*

1. From lines 1–4, we learn that rain appeared for Aeneas

    a. during the middle of winter   b. in open sea
    c. in sight of land   d. after it had detained the ships

2. A figure of speech in line 1 (*Postquam . . . ullae*) is

    a. hyperbole   b. chiasmus
    c. tmesis   d. metonymy

3. The metrical pattern of the first four feet of line 1 is

    a. spondee-dactyl-dactyl-spondee   b. dactyl-dactyl-dactyl-spondee
    c. spondee-dactyl-dactyl-dactyl   d. dactyl-spondee-dactyl-spondee

4. The case of *mihi* (line 3) is determined by

    a. *tum* (line 3)   b. *supra* (line 3)
    c. *caeruleus* (line 3)   d. *astitit* (line 3)

5. The word closest in meaning to *unda* (line 4) is
   a. *nimbus*
   b. *aqua*
   c. *fluctus*
   d. *hiems*

6. From line 4 we learn that
   a. the wave recoiled from the darkness
   b. the storm brought darkness
   c. the Trojans were sailing at night
   d. the rain bristled at the waves

7. The best translation of *iactamur* (line 6) is
   a. we hurl ourselves
   b. we are tossed
   c. we boast
   d. we cast

8. The form *involvere* (line 7) is
   a. present active infinitive
   b. present passive imperative
   c. future passive indicative
   d. perfect active indicative

9. The words *nox umida caelum abstulit* (lines 7–8) tell us that the
   a. storm obscured the sky
   b. sky was moist during the night
   c. night escaped with the sky
   d. humid sky retained sunlight

10. The subject of *negat* (line 10) is
    a. the storm
    b. Aeneas
    c. an understood *nox*
    d. Palinurus

11. The passage states that the ship's location was
    a. discerned by the stars
    b. unknown
    c. discerned by lightning flashes
    d. in a whirlpool

12. The case and number of *media* (line 11) are
    a. nominative singular
    b. accusative plural
    c. nominative plural
    d. ablative singular

13. The case of *viae* (line 11) is determined by
    a. *meminisse* (line 11)
    b. *unda* (line 11)
    c. *media* (line 11)
    d. *Palinurus* (line 11)

PASSAGE D

Catullus addresses his farm.

O funde noster seu Sabine seu Tiburs	
(nam te esse Tiburtem autumant, quibus non est	
cordi Catullum laedere; at quibus cordi est,	
quovis Sabinum pignore esse contendunt),	
sed seu Sabine sive verius Tiburs,	5
fui libenter in tua suburbana	
villa, malamque pectore expuli tussim,	
non inmerenti quam mihi meus venter,	
dum sumptuosas appeto, dedit, cenas.	
Nam, Sestianus dum volo esse conviva,	10
orationem in Antium petitorem	
plenam veneni et pestilentiae legi.	
Hic me gravido frigida et frequens tussis	
quassavit usque, dum in tuum sinum fugi,	
et me recuravi otioque et urtica.	15
Quare refectus maximas tibi grates	
ago, meum quod non es ulta peccatum.	

fundus, -i, m. *farm*
Sabinus, -a, -um, *Sabine* (of a modest hill district outside Rome)
Tiburs, -tis, *Tiburtine* (of modern Tivoli, a high-class district outside Rome)
autumo, -are, -avi, -atum, *to claim, assert*
quivis, quaevis, quodvis, *any one that you want, any at all*
pignus, pignoris, n. *pledge*
tussis, tussis, f. *cough*
inmerens, -ntis, *undeserving*
venter, ventris, m. *stomach*
sumptuosus, -a, -um, *expensive, luxurious*
petitor, -oris, m. *candidate for political office*
gravido, -dinis, f. *head cold*
quasso, -are, -avi, -atum, *to shake*
usque, *continually*
urtica, -ae, f. *nettle* (a weed often made into a medicinal tea)
ulciscor, -isci, ultus sum, *to punish, avenge*
peccatum, -i, n. *sin*

1. The word *quibus* (line 2) refers to

   a. *funde* (line 1)

   b. *Sabine* (line 1)

   c. *Tiburtem* (line 2)

   d. the subject of *autumant* (line 2)

2. In line 3, the case of *cordi* is

    a. dative

    b. nominative

    c. genitive

    d. ablative

3. According to lines 2–4, Catullus is annoyed when people say that his farm

    a. is not fertile

    b. does not belong to him

    c. is Sabine

    d. is Tiburtine

4. The discussion of the farm in lines 1–5 is primarily concerned with

    a. whether or not it is convenient to Rome

    b. whether or not it is fashionable

    c. the beauty of its setting

    d. the size of its fields

5. In lines 1–6, the phrase in which Catullus tells how he felt about staying in the country is

    a. *te esse Tiburtem autumant* (line 2)

    b. *Catullum laedere* (line 3)

    c. *quovis . . . pignore esse contendunt* (line 4)

    d. *fui libenter in tua suburbana villa* (lines 6–7)

6. In line 7, *malam(que)* refers to

    a. Catullus' cough

    b. Catullus' indigestion

    c. the villa that Catullus had inherited

    d. a woman whom Catullus had forced to leave his villa

7. A figure of speech that appears in line 8 is

    a. asyndeton

    b. hyperbole

    c. litotes

    d. metonymy

8. The direct object of *dedit* (line 9) is

    a. *pectore* (line 7)

    b. *quam* (line 8)

    c. *venter* (line 8)

    d. *cenas* (line 9)

9. From line 10, we learn that

    a. Sestius wanted to come to Catullus' dinner party

    b. Catullus lived with Sestius for a while

    c. Catullus flew off to Sestius' house

    d. Sestius was hosting a dinner party

10. In lines 7–12 , Catullus describes the negative effect of Sestius' speech on him. Which of the following is another writer of whose work Catullus does not approve?

    a. Calvus

    b. Cinna

    c. Volusius

    d. Caecilius

11. In line 14, *dum* is translated

    a. although

    b. then

    c. until

    d. as long as

12. From lines 10–15, we can infer that

    a. the speech made Catullus sick

    b. a coughing fit made Catullus leave his farm

    c. Catullus was exiled because of politics

    d. Catullus suffered from chills because of the plague

13. In lines 16–17, we learn that Catullus

    a. is grateful to the farm for his recovery

    b. is guilty of having offended Antius

    c. thanks his friend for his help

    d. regrets his earlier behavior towards Sestius

ANSWER KEY

Passage A

1—b	5—b	9—a
2—d	6—d	10—d
3—a	7—c	11—a
4—c	8—d	12—b

Passage B

1—d	5—b	9—c
2—a	6—a	10—d
3—c	7—d	11—c
4—a	8—c	12—b
		13—a

Passage C

1—b	5—b	9—a
2—d	6—b	10—d
3—a	7—b	11—b
4—d	8—d	12—d
		13—a

Passage D

1—d	5—d	9—d
2—a	6—a	10—c
3—c	7—c	11—c
4—b	8—b	12—a
		13—a

VOCABULARY

In general, only long vowels in metrically indeterminate positions are marked. For example, the length of the "a" in "accipiter" need not be marked as long or short because the syllable in which it is contained must be long, regardless of the length of the vowel, because the vowel is followed by two consonants, "cc," (not a combination like "tr" which can create indeterminacy), while the "a" in "beātus" must be marked long because it occurs in a position where metrical rules cannot determine the length of the syllable in which it occurs.

A

ā/ab, prep. with abl., *from, by*

abeō, abīre, abiī, abitum, *go away, depart*

abrumpō, abrumpere, abrūpī, abruptum, *break, break apart*

absum, abesse, āfuī, āfutūrus, *be away, be absent*

absūmō, absūmere, absumpsī, absumptum, *spend, consume*

ac, conj., *and*

accendō, accendere, accendī, accensum, *kindle, arouse, ignite*

accipiter, accipitris, m., *hawk*

accurrō, accurrere, accurrī/accucurrī, accursum, *run or hurry up to*

Achaemenius, -a, -um, adj., *Persian, Parthian*

acūtus, -a, -um, adj., *sharp, severe*

ad, prep. with acc., *to, towards, near*

adferō, adferre, attulī, allātum, *bring, add*

adiciō, adicere, adiēcī, adiectum, *throw to, add*

adimō, adimere, adēmī, ademptum, *take away*

aditus, -ūs, m., *approach, access*

adiūtor, adiūtōris, m., *helper*

adlabōrō, adlabōrāre, *add to by taking trouble*

adolescō, adolescere, adolēvī, adultum, *grow up*, (of a season or time) *reach its peak*

adpōnō, adpōnere, adposuī, adpositum, *add; treat as, count as* (with **lucrum**)

adrogans, adrogantis, adj., *arrogant, insolent*

adsector, adsectārī, adsectātus sum, *follow closely, attend, escort*

adsum, adesse, adfuī, *be present; in technical sense, be present in court as a friend or adviser*

adurgeō, adurgēre, *press hard upon, pursue closely*

adventus, -ūs, m., *arrival, approach*

adversārius, adversāriī, m., *adversary, opponent*

Aenēās, Aenēae, m., *Aeneas*, son of Venus and Anchises, Trojan leader who brought his followers to Italy after the Trojan War and founded what would become the Roman state; hero of Vergil's *Aeneid*

aēneus, -a, -um, adj., *of bronze*

Aeolidēs, Aeolidae, m., *a son or more remote descendant of Aeolus*

Aeolius, -a, -um, adj., *Aeolian, Aeolic;* referring to Aeolia, the Greek area of Asia Minor, including the island of Lesbos where the Greek poets Sappho and Alcaeus lived, as well as to the dialect of Greek in which they wrote

aequor, aequoris, n., *a flat level surface, the flat surface of the sea,* (often used in pl.)

aequus, -a, -um, adj., *equal, even, impartial, fair*

āēr, āeris, m., *air, weather, mist*

aerātus, -a, -um, adj., *made of or fitted with bronze or brass*

aes, aeris, n., *copper, bronze, money*

aesculētum, -ī, n., *oak forest*

aestās, aestātis, f., *summer*

aestīvus, -a, -um, adj., *summer*

aestuōsus, -a, -um, adj., *very hot, agitated*

aetās, aetātis, f., *time, age*

aeternus, -a, -um, adj., *eternal, everlasting*

Āfricus, -a, -um, adj., *African*

ager, agrī, m., *field, territory*

agitō, agitāre, agitāvī, agitātum, *stir, drive, agitate, excite*

agō, agere, ēgī, actum, *do, drive*

agrestis, -e, adj., *of the country, rustic, rural*

āiō, defective verb, *say yes, say*

albus, -a, -um, adj., *white, bright*

aliās, adv., *at another time*

aliēnus, -a, -um, adj., *of another, alien, strange* (with abl. or dat.)

alius, alia, aliud, adj., *other, another*

almus, -a, -um, adj., *providing nurture, kindly, gracious*

alō, alere, aluī, altum, *nourish*

alter, altera, alterum, adj., *another, one of two, the one, the other*

altum, -ī, n., *high place or position, heaven, sea, the deep*

altus, -a, -um, adj., *high, deep, tall*

amābilis, -e, adj., *lovable, delightful*

amīcus, -ī, m., *friend*

amō, amāre, amāvī, amātum, *love*

amoenus, -a, -um, adj., *charming, pleasing*

amor, amōris, m., *love*

amplius, adv., *more*

amplus, -a, -um, adj., *large, spacious*

an, conj., *whether, or*

Ancus, -ī, m., *Ancus Martius,* fourth king of Rome

angiportus, -ūs, m., *alley*

angulus, -ī, m., *angle, corner*

angustus, -a, -um, adj., *narrow, limited, difficult* (of circumstances)

anima, -ae, f., *breath, life, darling*

animōsus, -a, -um, adj., *spirited, bold*

animus, -ī, m., *mind; mind, as standing for the whole person*

annus, -ī, m., *year*

antehāc, adv., *previously*

antestor, antestārī, antestātus sum, *call as a witness*

antrum, -ī, n., *cave, hollow space*

anus, -ūs, f., *old woman*

aper, aprī, m., *wild boar*

apium, apiī, n., *parsley, celery*

Apollō, Apollinis, m., *Apollo,* son of Jupiter and Latona, brother of Diana, god of archery, music, poetry, etc.

apparātus, -ūs, m., *preparation, show, sumptuousness, paraphernalia*

appāreō, appārēre, appāruī, appāritum, *appear*

aqua, -ae, f., *water, body of water*

Aquilō, Aquilōnis, m., *the north wind*

arbiter, arbitrī, m., *judge, overseer*

arbitrium, arbitriī, n., *decision, judgement*

arbor, arboris, f., *tree*

arbustum, -ī, n., *wood, plantation,* (pl.) *trees*

arbutus, -ī, f., *the wild strawberry or arbutus tree*

arceō, arcēre, arcuī, *contain, keep away, spurn*

Arctūrus, -ī, m., *Arcturus,* the brightest star of the constellation Boōtes

arcus, -ūs, m., *bow*

ardeō, ardēre, arsī, *be on fire, burn, be in love* (with abl.)

arduus, -a, -um, adj., *steep, towering, lofty, high, difficult*

ārea, -ae, f., *open space, threshing floor*

arguō, arguere, arguī, argūtum, *prove, show*

āridus, -a, -um, adj., *dry*

Aristius, Aristiī, m., *Aristius Fuscus,* Horace's literary friend; cf. Satire 1.9 and Ode 1.22

arripiō, arripere, arripuī, arreptum, *seize, take hold of, arrest, bring before a court*

artus, -a, -um, adj., *close, thrifty, dense, economical*

asellus, -ī, m., *young ass, young donkey*

asper, aspera, asperum, adj., *fierce, rough*

at, conj., *but*

atavus, -ī, m., *a great-great-great grandfather, or remote ancestor*

āter, ātra, ātrum, adj., *black, dark, gloomy*

atque, conj., *and;* after comparatives, *than;* also, cf. **simul**

atquī, conj., *but, nevertheless*

ātrium, ātriī, n., *hall, first main room in a Roman-style house*

atrox, atrōcis, adj., *dreadful, fierce, cruel*

Attalicus, -a, -um, adj., *of King Attalus or his dynasty, rich, splendid*

audeō, audēre, ausus sum, *dare, wish*

audiō, audīre, audīvī, audītum, *hear, heed*

auferō, auferre, abstulī, ablātum, *take away, carry off, kill*

Aufidus, -ī, m., *Aufidus,* river in Apulia

aula, aulae, f., *noble residence, palace, hall*

aura, -ae, f., *breeze*

aureus, -a, -um, adj., *golden, splendid*

auricula, -ae, f., *ear*

auris, auris, f., *ear*

Auster, Austrī, m., *south wind*

aut, conj., *or;* **aut . . . aut,** *either . . . or*

autumnus, -ī, m., *autumn*

avidus, -a, -um, adj., *greedy, avaricious, eager*

avis, avis, f., *bird*

avītus, -a, -um, adj., *of a grandfather, ancestral*

āvius, -a, -um, adj., *pathless, remote*

B

Babylōnius, -a, -um, adj., *Babylonian*

bacchor, bacchārī, bacchātus sum, *celebrate the festival of Bacchus, rave, rage*

Bandusia, -ae, f., *Bandusia,* name of a spring, perhaps at Horace's Sabine farm or near Apulia, the area on which his hometown bordered

barbarē, adv., *roughly, cruelly*

barbitos, barbitī, m., *lyre*

beātus, -a, -um, adj., *happy, fortunate*

bellum, -ī, n., *war*

bene, adv., *well;* with adj. or adv., *quite*

benignē, adv., *lavishly, liberally*

beō, beāre, beāvī, beātum, *bless, make happy*

bibō, bibere, bibī, *drink*

bīlis, bīlis, f., *gall, bile, anger*

bis, adv., *twice*

blandus, -a, -um, adj., *charming, persuasive, seductive*

Bōlānus, -ī, m., *Bolanus,* Roman cognomen

bonus, -a, -um, adj., *good*

brāchium, brāchiī, n., *arm*

brevis, -e, adj., *short, brief*

brūma, -ae, f., *the shortest day, winter, wintry weather*

Brūtus, -ī, m., *Marcus Iunius Brutus,* one of the leaders, along with Cassius, of the conspiracy to kill Julius Caesar.

C

cadō, cadere, cecidī, cāsum, *fall, die, set* (of heavenly bodies)

cadus, -ī, m., *jar, flask* (especially for wine)

Caecubum, -ī, n., *choice wine from Caecubum,* a district in south Latium

caelestis, -e, adj., *of the sky, celestial, divine*

caelum, -ī, n., *sky, heavens, weather, world*

caementum, -ī, n., *small stones, rubble*

Caesar, Caesaris, m., *Caesar;* Octavian (later Augustus), in Ode 1.37; in Satire 1.9, Julius Caesar, (100–44 BCE), Roman general who defeated Pompey at the battle of Pharsalus in 48 BCE and was made dictator for life in 44 BCE, shortly before his assassination in the conspiracy led by Brutus and Cassius.

Calais, Calais, m., *Calais,* man's name

campus, -ī, m., *plain, level surface; plain, field;* often refers specifically to the Campus Martius in Rome

candidus, -a, -um, adj., *bright, radiant, white*

canīcula, -ae, f., *the Dog Star, Sirius,* in the constellation Canis Major, brightest star in the sky, thought to bring hot weather

canitiēs, canitiēī, f., *white or grey coloring, grey or white hair*

canō, canere, cecinī, cantum, *sing, sing about, recite, prophesy, foretell*

cantō, cantāre, cantāvī, cantātum, *sing, sing about, recite*

cantus, -ūs, m., *singing, song, poetry*

capax, capācis, adj., *spacious, capable*

Capitōlium, Capitōliī, n., *Capitolium,* the Capitoline hill in Rome on which the Capitoline gods, Jupiter, Juno, and Minerva, were worshipped

caput, capitis, n., *head, top, source, person, person's life*

cardō, cardinis, m., *hinge*

careō, carēre, caruī, caritum, *lack, be without* (with abl.)

carmen, carminis, n., *solemn or ritual utterance, song, poem, lyric poetry*

carpō, carpere, carpsī, carptum, *pluck, seize*

cārus, -a, -um, adj., *dear, beloved*

castra, castrōrum, n. pl., *military camp*

cāsus, -ūs, m., *fall, event, misfortune, chance*

catēna, -ae, f., *chain*

catulus, -ī, m., *a young animal,* especially *a young dog*

Caucasus, -ī, m., *Caucasus mountains*

cautus, -a, -um, adj., *on one's guard, wary, cautious, prudent*

cavus, -a, -um, adj., *hollow, concave*

cēdō, cēdere, cessī, cessum, *go, yield, withdraw*

celer, celeris, celere, adj., *swift, quick*

cella, -ae, f., *storeroom, wine cellar*

celsus, -a, -um, adj., *high, lofty, proud*

cēna, -ae, f., *dinner*

centum, indecl.adj., *a hundred*

cerebrum, -ī, n., *brain, seat of intelligence, seat of anger, anger*

cēreus, -a, -um, adj., *waxen, supple*

certō, certāre, certāvī, certātum, *contend, strive*

certus, -a, -um, adj., *certain, definite*

cerva, -ae, f., *deer, female deer*

cervix, cervīcis, f., *neck*

cēterus, -a, -um, adj., *the rest,* usually found in plural

Chloē, Chloēs, f., *Chloe,* Greek woman's name

chorēa, -ae, f., *dance*

chorus, -ī, m., *choral dance, people singing and dancing, crowd, troop*

cibōrium, cibōriī, n., *a kind of drinking cup*

cingō, cingere, cinxī, cinctum, *surround, encircle*

circā, prep. with acc., *around*

circumagō, circumagere, circumēgī, circumactum, *drive or lead around, lead around in circles*

cithara, -ae, f., *lyre*

citius, adv., *quicker, sooner*

citus, -a, -um, adj., *swift, quick*

cīvīlis, -e, adj., *civil*

clāmor, clāmōris, m., *shout, shouting, clamor*

clārus, -a, -um, adj., *clear, bright, famous*

classis, classis, f., *fleet, political class*

clāvis, clāvis, f., *key*

cliens, clientis, m., *client;* one who attaches himself to a person of greater influence or political power (**patrōnus**) for protection

Cōcȳtos, Cōcȳtī, m., *Cocytus,* one of the rivers of the underworld

coemō, coemere, coēmī, coemptum, *buy up*

coepī, coepisse, coeptum (typically appears in perfect system), *begin*

cognātus, -a, -um, adj., *related*

cōgō, cōgere, coēgī, coactum, *drive together, force*

cohibeō, cohibēre, cohibuī, cohibitum, *hold together, hold back, confine*

colligō, colligere, collēgī, collectum, *to gather or bring together, collect*

colō, colere, coluī, cultum, *cultivate, cherish*

colōnus, -ī, m., *farmer, settler*

color, colōris, m., *color*

columba, -ae, f., *dove, pigeon*

coma, -ae, f., *hair*

combibō, combibere, combibī, *drink up, drink completely*

compellō, compellere, compulī, compulsum, *bring together, drive together, round up*

compescō, compescere, compescuī, *confine, restrain, check*

compōnō, compōnere, composuī, compositum, *put together, arrange, compose, calm, bury*

concha, -ae, f., *shell fish, sea shell, perfume dish*

concursus, -ūs, m., *running to and fro*

condiciō, condiciōnis, f., *condition, term, agreement*

condō, condere, condidī, conditum, *found, establish, store up*

conficiō, conficere, confēcī, confectum, *complete, destroy, finish off, kill*

coniunx, coniugis, c., *spouse, wife, husband*

consistō, consistere, constitī, *stop, pause, stand still, take a position*

consociō, consociāre, consociāvī, consociātum, *unite, connect, share*

constō, constāre, constitī, *stand together, stand still*

consūmō, consūmere, consumpsī, consumptum, *consume, destroy, kill*

contāminātus, -a, -um, adj., *morally foul, impure*

contendō, contendere, contendī, contentum, *stretch, hasten, compete, contend*

contrahō, contrahere, contraxī, contractum, *draw together, narrow*

cōpula, -ae, f., *bond, link*

cor, cordis, n., *heart*

cornū, -ūs, n., *horn, anything horn-shaped*

corōna, -ae, f., *crown, garland*

corōnō, corōnāre, corōnāvī, corōnātum, *put a garland on, crown*

corpus, corporis, n., *body*

corrigō, corrigere, correxī, correctum, *make straight, correct, remedy*

corrumpō, corrumpere, corrūpī, corruptum, *damage, spoil, bribe, seduce*

cortex, corticis, m., *bark, rind, cork*

costum, -ī, n., *an aromatic plant*

crās, adv., *tomorrow*

crastinus, -a, -um, adj., *of tomorrow*

crēber, crēbra, crēbrum, adj., *crowded together, frequent*

crēdibilis, -e, adj., *believable*

crēdō, crēdere, crēdidī, crēditum, *trust, believe, entrust*

crēdulus, -a, -um, adj., *credulous, trustful*

crescō, crescere, crēvī, crētum, *arise, multiply, expand, increase*

cruentus, -a, -um, adj., *bloody, gory, cruel*

cubō, cubāre, cubuī, cubitum, *lie down or be lying down, recline, be in bed or on one's couch, be confined to bed by illness, recline at table*

culpō, culpāre, culpāvī, culpātum, *blame*

culter, cultrī, m., *knife*

cum, prep. with abl., *with;* conj., *when, since, although*

cumba, -ae, f., *small boat,* especially that in which Charon ferries the dead across the river Styx

cunctus, -a, -um, adj., *the whole of, all*

cupiō, cupere, cupīvī, cupītum, *wish, desire, long for*

cupressus, -ī, f., *cypress*

cūr, adv., *why*

cūra, -ae, f., *care, concern, worry,* a person or thing constituting an object of care

cūrō, cūrāre, cūrāvī, cūrātum, *care about, take care of, attend to*

curriculum, -ī, n., *a running, course, race, racing chariot*

currus, -ūs, m., *chariot*

curtus, -a, -um, adj., *having a part missing, mutilated, circumcized*

Cyprius, -a, -um, adj., *Cyprian, of the island of Cyprus*

D

damnō, damnāre, damnāvī, damnātum, *condemn, sentence*

damnum, -ī, n., *loss*

Danaus, -ī, m., *Danaus;* all but one of his fifty daughters, the Danaids, on instructions from their father, killed their husbands on their wedding night; they are punished in the underworld by having continuously to fill up leaky jars

daps, dapis, f., *feast, banquet*

Daunias, Dauniadis, f., *Apulia,* region of southeastern Italy

Daunus, -ī, m., *Daunus,* legendary king of Apulia

dē, prep. with abl., *about, concerning, down from, from*

dēbeō, dēbēre, dēbuī, dēbitum, *owe, ought, should, must*

dēbilitō, dēbilitāre, dēbilitāvī, dēbilitātum, *weaken*

dēcēdō, dēcēdere, dēcessī, dēcessum, *go away, depart, withdraw* (with abl.)

dēcidō, dēcidere, dēcidī, *fall down, die*

dēcrescō, dēcrescere, dēcrēvī, dēcrētum, *decrease, grow smaller, shrink*

decus, decoris, n., *that which adorns or beautifies, honor, glory*

dēdecet, dēdecēre, dēdecuit, used in third person, *be unsuitable for, be unbecoming to*

dēdicō, dēdicāre, dēdicāvī, dēdicātum, *dedicate*

dēdūcō, dēdūcere, dēduxi, dēductum, *lead away, lead down, escort, bring a person or army back with one to Rome, bring home in procession as a bride, spin, compose, adapt*

dēlēniō, dēlēnīre, dēlēnīvī, dēlēnītum, *soothe*

dēlīberō, dēlīberāre, dēlīberāvī, dēlīberātum, *consider carefully, deliberate, decide*

Dellius, Delliī, m., *Quintus Dellius,* who first joined Dolabella, then Cassius, then Antony, and finally Octavian, right before Actium

Delphicus, -a, -um, adj., *Delphic, of Delphi* (the site of the oracle of Apollo, god of poetry and the arts, among other things)

dēmens, dēmentis, adj., *out of one's senses, mad, insane*

dēmittō, dēmittere, dēmīsī, dēmissum, *let down, let fall, lower, sink*

dēmō, dēmere, dempsī, demptum, *take away, subtract*

dēmoveō, dēmovēre, dēmōvī, dēmōtum, *remove, drive out*

dens, dentis, m., *tooth*

densus, -a, -um, adj., *thick, dense*

dēpōnō, dēpōnere, dēposuī, dēpositum, *lay down*

dēproelior, dēproeliārī, *fight fiercely, struggle violently*

dēprōmō, dēprōmere, dēprompsī, dēpromptum, *bring out, produce*

dēproperō, dēproperāre, *hurry to complete*

dēripiō, dēripere, dēripuī, dēreptum, *tear down, snatch away*

descendō, descendere, descendī, descensum, *come or go down, descend*

dēsīderium, desideriī, n., *desire, longing* (for something or someone lost or absent)

dēsīderō, dēsīderāre, dēsīderāvī, dēsīderātum, *desire, want, long for*

dēsiliō, dēsilīre, dēsiluī, *leap or jump down*

dēsinō, dēsinere, dēsiī, dēsitum, *stop, cease*

dēsistō, dēsistere, destitī, *cease, desist*

destinō, destināre, destināvī, destinātum, *fix, determine, intend, destine, earmark*

destringō, destringere, destrinxī, districtum, *strip off, scrape lightly, draw or unsheathe* (a weapon)

dēsum, dēesse, dēfuī, *be missing, fail* (with dat. of person)

dētestor, dētestārī, dētestātus sum, *pray against, curse*

deus, -ī, m., *god;* **dī,** alternate form of **deī,** nom. pl., **dīs,** alternate form of **deīs,** dat. and abl. pl.

dexter, dextra, dextrum, adj., *right, skillful*

Diāna, -ae, f., *the goddess Diana,* daughter of Jupiter and Latona

dīcō, dīcere, dixī, dictum, *say, tell, call*

dīdūcō, dīdūcere, dīduxī, dīductum, *separate, split*

diēs, diēī, m., (f.) *day*

difficilis, -e, adj., *difficult, troublesome, hard to manage*

diffugiō, diffugere, diffūgī, *flee in several directions, disperse, scatter*

digitus, -ī, m., *finger*

dignus, -a, -um, adj., *worthy, worthy of, deserving* (with abl.)

dīligō, dīligere, dīlexī, dīlectum, *love, esteem, hold dear, have special regard for*

dīmoveō, dīmovēre, dīmōvī, dīmōtum, *move apart, separate*

diōta, -ae, f., *two-handled wine jar*

dīruō, dīruere, dīruī, dīrutum, *cause to fall in ruin, demolish*

dīrus, -a, -um, adj., *terrible, awful, dire*

dīs, dītis, adj., *rich, wealthy*

discēdō, discēdere, discessi, discessum, *go away, depart*

dispereō, disperīre, disperiī, *perish, be destroyed* (frequently hyperbolic)

displiceō, displicēre, displicuī, displicitum, *displease*

dissimulō, dissimulāre, dissimulāvī, dissimulātum, *pretend that something is not what it is, pretend not to notice, ignore*

dissolvō, dissolvere, dissolvī, dissolūtum, *dissolve, free*

distorqueō, distorquēre, distorsī, distortum, *twist this way and that, distort, torment*

dīvellō, dīvellere, dīvellī, dīvolsum, *tear apart*

dīves, dīvitis, adj., *rich, wealthy*

dīvīnus, -a, -um, adj., *divine*

dīvitiae, dīvitiārum, f. pl., *wealth, riches*

dīvum, -ī, n., *sky*

dīvus, -a, -um, adj., *divine*

dīvus, -ī, m., *god*

dō, dare, dedī, datum, *give*

doctus, -a, -um, *learned, taught*

doleō, dolēre, doluī, dolitum, *suffer mental or physical pain, be in pain, grieve*

dolor, dolōris, m., *pain, anguish, grief*

dominus, -ī, m., *master, lord, ruler*

domus, -ūs/-ī, f., *house, home*

dōnec, conj., *as long as, while*

dōnō, dōnāre, dōnāvī, dōnātum, *present, endow, reward* (with), with abl. of thing given

dormiō, dormīre, dormīvī, dormītum, *sleep*

dorsum, -ī, n., *back*

dubius, -a, -um, adj., *uncertain, indecisive*

dūcō, dūcere, duxī, ductum, *lead, take, consider*

dudum, adv., *some time ago, previously, just now; for a long time* (with **iam**)

dulce, adv., *sweetly*

dulcis, -e, adj., *sweet,* (of persons) *dear, beloved*

dum, conj., *while, as long as, provided that, if only, until*

dūrus, -a, -um, adj., *hard, harsh*

dux, ducis, m., *leader, general, commander*

E

ē/ex, prep. with abl., *out of, from*

ēbrius, -a, -um, adj., *drunk*

ecce, interj., *look, behold*

edax, edācis, adj., *greedy, devouring, destructive*

ēditus, -a, -um, adj. (from **ēdo**), *descended from*

ēdō, ēdere, ēdidī, ēditum, *put forth, give out, give birth to*

Ēdōnus, -a, -um, adj., *Thracian;* the **Ēdōnī** were a tribe celebrated for their orgiastic worship of Bacchus

effundō, effundere, effūdī, effūsum, *pour out, pour forth*

egeō, egēre, eguī, *need, want* (with abl.)

ego, meī, mihi/mī, mē, mē, pron., *I, me*

ēheu, interj. (expressing grief or pain), *alas*

ēlabōrō, ēlabōrāre, ēlabōrāvī, ēlabōrātum, *strive, work out, develop, perfect*

ēmīror, ēmīrārī, *wonder at exceedingly, be astonished at*

ēnāvigō, ēnāvigāre, ēnāvigāvī, ēnāvigātum, *sail across, sail forth*

enim, conj., *for, truly*

ensis, ensis, m., *sword*

eō, adv., abl. of **is**, *therefore*

eō, īre, īvī/iī, itum, *go*

eōdem, adv., *to the same place*

eques, equitis, m., *horseman, rider, member of the cavalry, member of the equestrian order*

equus, -ī, m., *horse*

ergō, particle, *then, consequently, therefore*

ēripiō, ēripere, ēripuī, ēreptum, *snatch away, rescue*

errō, errāre, errāvī, errātum, *wander, make a mistake*

et, conj., *and, even;* et . . . et, *both . . . and*

Euterpē, Euterpēs, f., *Euterpe, one of the Muses.*

ēvehō, ēvehere, ēvexī, ēvectum, *carry out, lift up, raise*

ēvītō, ēvītāre, ēvītāvī, ēvītātum, *avoid*

exclūdō, exclūdere, exclūsī, exclūsum, *shut out, exclude*

excutiō, excutere, excussī, excussum, *shake out, drive out, banish*

exeō, exīre, exiī, exitum, *go out, come out, emerge*

exigō, exigere, exēgī, exactum, *drive out, complete, execute*

exilium, exiliī, n., *exile*

expavescō, expavescere, expāvī, *become frightened of, dread*

expediō, expedīre, expedīvī, expedītum, *free, extricate, release*

expleō, explēre, explēvī, explētum, *fill up*

expugnō, expugnāre, expugnāvī, expugnātum, *storm, conquer, overcome*

exstruō, exstruere, exstruxī, exstructum, *heap up, pile up, construct*

F

fābulōsus, -a, -um, adj., *legendary, storied*

facilis, -e, adj., *easy, quick*

faciō, facere, fēcī, factum, *make, do, regard*

fācundia, -ae, f., *eloquence*

Falernum, -ī, n., *Falernian wine,* wine from a district in northern Campania famous for its wine

Falernus, -a, -um, adj., *Falernian,* of a district in northern Campania famous for its wine

fallax, fallācis, adj., *deceitful, deceptive*

fāma, -ae, f., *fame, reputation*

famulus, -ī, m., *servant, attendant, slave*

fastīdiō, fastīdīre, fastīdīvī, fastīdītum, *show aversion to, scorn*

fastīdiōsus, -a, -um, adj., *critical, exacting, disdainful*

fātālis, -e, adj., *deadly, fatal*

fātum, -ī, n., *fate,* pl., *the Fates*

faveō, favēre, fāvī, fautum, *favor;* with linguīs (abl.), *avoid words of ill omen, be silent*

fax, facis, f., *torch, torch used at funerals and marriages, marriage, death*

fēlix, fēlīcis, adj., *happy, fortunate*

fenestra, -ae, f., *window*

feriō, ferīre, *strike, hit*

ferō, ferre, tulī, lātum, *bear, bring, carry, play* (a part, role)

ferox, ferōcis, adj., *bold*

fervens, ferventis, adj., *boiling, seething*

fervidus, -a, -um, adj., *boiling, burning, hot, impetuous*

fessus, -a, -um, adj., *tired, weary*

festus, -a, -um, adj., *festal, on holiday, festive*

fidēlis, -e, adj., *faithful*

fidēs, fideī, f., *trust, belief, faith, honesty, honor*

fidēs, fidis, f., *lyre*

filius, filiī, m., *son*

fīlum, -ī, n., *thread*

findō, findere, fidī, fissum, *split, separate, divide*

fīnis, fīnis, m., *boundary, limit, end*

fīō, fīerī, factus sum, *be made, become*

flagrans, flagrantis, adj., *hot, blazing, passionate*

flāvus, -a, -um, adj., *yellow, golden, blonde, auburn*

flēbilis, -e, adj., *worthy of tears, lamentable*

fleō, flēre, flēvī, flētum, *weep for, lament*

flōs, flōris, m., *flower*

fluctus, -ūs, m., *a flowing, wave, disturbance*

flūmen, flūminis, n., *river, waters of a river*

focus, -ī, m., *hearth, fireplace*

folium, foliī, n., *leaf*

fons, fontis, m., *spring, source*

fors, fortis, f., *chance, luck*

forte, adv., *by chance, as luck would have it, as it so happened*

fortis, -e, adj., *brave*

fortūna, -ae, f., *fortune, chance, luck*

frangō, frangere, frēgī, fractum, *break, crush*

frequens, frequentis, adj., *crowded, assiduous, constant, regular*

fretum, -ī, n., *strait, sea, violence*

frīgidus, -a, -um, *cold*

frīgus, frigoris, n., *cold*

frons, frondis, f., *leaf*

frons, frontis, f., *forehead, brow, front*

fruor, fruī, fructus sum, *enjoy* (with abl.)

frustrā, adv., *in vain, to no purpose*

frux, frūgis, f., usually in pl., *fruit, crops*

fuga, -ae, f., *flight, rout*

fugax, fugācis, adj., *swift, fugitive, elusive*

fugiō, fugere, fūgī, fugitum, *flee, flee from, avoid*

fulgur, fulguris, n., *a flash of lightning, flash of light*

fundō, fundere, fūdī, fūsum, *pour, spread, scatter, defeat*

fundus, -ī, m., *bottom, farm, estate*

fūnus, fūneris, n., *funeral, death, destruction*

furens, furentis, adj., *mad, wild*

furiō, furiāre, furiāvī, furiātum, *madden*

furō, furere, *behave wildly, be crazy*

furor, furōris, m., *madness, frenzy, fury*

furtim, adv., *secretly*

Fuscus, -ī, m., *Aristius Fuscus,* Horace's literary friend; cf. *Satire* 1.9 and *Ode* 1.22

G

Gaetūlus, -a, -um, adj., *Gaetulian, of Gaetulia,* region of northwest Africa known for its lions

garriō, garrīre, garrīvī, *talk rapidly, chatter,* (do this in writing)

garrulus, -a, -um, adj., *talkative, loquacious*

gaudeō, gaudēre, gāvīsus sum, *rejoice, delight in* (with abl.)

gelidus, -a, -um, adj., *cold, icy*

gelū, -ūs, n., *frost, cold, chill*

geminus, -a, -um, adj., *twin, double*

gena, -ae, f., *cheek*

generō, generāre, generāvī, generātum, *produce, create*

generōsē, adv., *nobly, with dignity*

generōsus, -a, -um, adj., *of noble birth, noble*

gens, gentis, f., *clan, tribe, family*

genū, -ūs, n., *knee*

genus, generis, n., *birth, race, kind, offspring*

Gēryōn, Gēryonis, m., *Geryon;* triple-headed or triple-bodied king whom Hercules killed when carrying off his cattle

Gigantēus, -a, -um, adj., *of the Giants,* a mythical race, who fought and were defeated by the Olympian gods

gracilis, -e, adj., *slender, thin*

grāmen, grāminis, n., *grass*

grandō, grandinis, f., *hail*

grātia, -ae, f., *goodwill, kindness, charm, attraction,* pl. personified, *the Graces,* goddesses (usually three in number) embodying charm and beauty

grātus, -a, -um, adj., *pleasing*

gravidus, -a, -um, adj., *laden, weighed down*

gravis, -e, adj., *heavy, weighty, serious*

grex, gregis, m., *flock, herd, company, crowd*

H

habeō, habēre, habuī, habitum, *have, hold, consider, keep*

Hadria, -ae, m., *Adriatic Sea*

haedus, -ī, m., *young goat, kid;* two stars in the constellation Auriga

Haemonia, -ae, f., *Thessaly*

haud, adv., *not*

Hebrus, -ī, m., *Hebrus,* river in Thrace

hedera, -ae, f., *ivy*

hērēs, hērēdis, c., *heir*

Hermogenēs, Hermogenis, m., *Hermogenes;* in Satire 1.10.80 Horace places a Hermogenes Tegellius in a group of people whose opinions do not matter to him as opposed to those of his literary friends.

heu, interj., expressing grief or pain, *oh, alas*

hīc, adv., *here, at this point*

hic, haec, hoc, demonstr. pron. and adj., *this, the latter*

hiems, hiemis, f., *winter, storm*

hinc, adv., *from here, here*

Hippolytus, -ī, m., *Hippolytus,* son of Theseus, whose rejection of the sexual advances of his stepmother, Phaedra, resulted in his death.

hodiē, adv., *today*

hodiernus, -a, -um, adj., *of today*

homō, hominis, m., *person, human being*

honor (honōs), honōris, m., *honor, office*

hōra, -ae, f., *hour, time, season*

horrescō, horrescere, horruī, *shudder at, tremble at*

horreum, -ī, n., *storehouse, granary*

horridus, -a, -um, adj., *rough, harsh, dreadful*

hortus, -ī, m., *garden;* usually in pl., *pleasure grounds or gardens*

hospitālis, -e, adj., *hospitable, belonging to a host or guest*

hosticus, -a, -um, adj., *belonging to an enemy*

hostis, hostis, c., *enemy*

hūc, adv., *to here, here*

humilis, -e, adj., *humble, low;* neuter as noun, *low position*

Hydaspēs, Hydaspis, m., *Hydaspes,* tributary of river Indus, the Jhelum

I

iaceō, iacēre, iacuī, *lie, be in ruins*

iaciō, iacere, iēcī, iactum, *throw, lay foundations*

iactus, -ūs, m., *throwing, hurling*

iaculum, -ī, n., *javelin*

iam, adv., *already, now*

iānua, -ae, f., *door*

Īcarius, -a, -um, adj., *of Icarus, Icarian*

īdem, eadem, idem, pron. and adj., *the same, too, likewise*

iecur, iecoris, n., *liver, the seat of the feelings*

ignis, ignis, m., *fire*

ignoscō, ignoscere, ignōvī, ignōtum, *forgive, pardon*

īlex, īlicis, f., *holm oak, ilex*

Īlia, -ae, f., *Ilia or Rhea Silvia,* mother of Romulus and Remus

ille, illa, illud, demonstr. pron. and adj., *that, the former*

illīc, adv., *there*

imāgō, imāginis, f., *image, likeness, shape*

imber, imbris, m., *rain, rain shower, water*

imbuō, imbuere, imbuī, imbūtum, *wet, fill, inspire*

imperium, imperiī, n., *power, command, government*

impetus, -ūs, m., *attack, onset, rapid motion*

impius, -a, -um, adj., *impious, undutiful, disloyal*

īmus, -a, -um, adj., *lowest, bottom of*

īn(n)uleus, -ī, m., *fawn*

in, prep. with abl., *in, on;* prep. with acc., *into, onto, against, over*

Īnachus, -ī, m., *Inachus,* first king of Argos

incipiō, incipere, incēpī, inceptum, *begin*

inclāmō, inclāmāre, inclāmāvī, inclāmātum, *call out, cry out*

incorruptus, -a, -um, adj., *uncorrupted, upright*

indicō, indicāre, indicāvī, indicātum, *point out, show, declare*

indocilis, -e, adj., *untrained, hard to instruct*

indomitus, -a, -um, adj., *unconquered, unconquerable*

inermis, -e, adj., *unarmed*

iners, inertis, adj., *lacking skill, inactive, lazy, impotent*

infāmis, -e, adj., *infamous, disreputable*

infernus, -a, -um, adj., *lower, of the lower world, infernal*

infestus, -a, -um, adj., *dangerous, hostile, insecure*

inficiō, inficere, infēcī, infectum, *dye, imbue, taint, stain*

infimus, -a, -um, adj., *lowest, most humble*

infirmus, -a, -um, adj., *weak, lacking strength of purpose, not resolute*

informis, -e, adj., *shapeless, deformed, ugly*

ingens, ingentis, adj., *huge*

inhorrescō, inhorrescere, inhorruī, *begin to tremble, bristle, become stiffly erect*

inhospitālis, -e, adj., *inhospitable*

inīquus, -a, -um, adj., *uneven, unfavorable, treacherous, discontented*

inlacrimābilis, -e, adj., *pitiless*

inmemor, inmemoris, adj., *forgetful, unmindful*

inmodicus, -a, -um, adj., *immoderate*

inmortālis, -e, adj., *immortal*

innumerābilis, -e, adj., *countless, numberless*

inops, inopis, adj., *lacking wealth, poor*

inpōnō, inpōnere, inposuī, inpositum, *place on or over, build on*

inpotens, inpotentis, adj., *powerless, weak, wild, violent*

inprimō, inprimere, inpressī, inpressum, *press upon*

inprobus, -a, -um, adj., *unprincipled, immoderate, unruly, relentless, shameless*

inquam, inquit, defective verb, only a few forms occur, most often used parenthetically or before or after a quotation, *say*

inruptus, -a, -um, *broken into, interrupted; unbroken*

inserō, inserere, inseruī, insertum, *introduce, insert, put in or among*

insignis, -e, adj., *distinguished*

insolens, insolentis, adj., *unaccustomed, excessive*

instans, instantis, adj., *pressing, urgent*

instō, instāre, institī, *be pressing, loom, threaten*

integer, integra, integrum, adj., *whole, untouched, upright*

intemptātus, -a, -um, adj., *untried, unattempted*

interdum, adv., *at times*

intereō, interīre, interiī, interitum, *perish, die*

interior, interius, adj., *inner, interior, private*

interlūnium, interlūniī, n., *the period between the old moon and the new*

interpellō, interpellāre, interpellāvī, interpellātum, *interrupt, break in on, impede*

intersum, interesse, interfuī, when used impersonally, *it makes a difference, it matters, it is of importance*

intumus, -a, -um, adj., *innermost, most secret*

inveniō, invenīre, invēnī, inventum, *find*

invicem, adv., *in turn*

invideō, invidēre, invīdī, invīsum, *envy, begrudge, refuse*

invidus, -a, -um, adj., *envious, jealous*

invīsus, -a, -um, adj., *hateful, odious*

ipse, ipsa, ipsum, pron., adj., *himself, herself, itself, oneself* etc.

īrācundus, -a, -um, adj., *angry, hot-tempered, prone to anger*

is, ea, id, pron. and adj., *he, she, it, this, that*

iste, ista, istud, pron. and adj., *that of yours, this, that* (often with derogatory sense)

ita, adv., *thus, so*

Italia, -ae, f., *Italy*

Italus, -a, -um, adj., *Italian*

iter, itineris, n., *journey*

Iuba, -ae, m., *Juba;* Juba I, Numidian king who supported Pompey in the civil war; Juba II, son of Juba I, fought for Octavian (Augustus) at the battle of Actium, made king of Mauretania by Augustus, known for his learning

iubeō, iubēre, iussī, iussum, *order, command, bid*

Iūdaeus, -ī, m., *Jew*

iugum, -ī, n., *yoke, bond*

iungō, iungere, iunxī, iunctum, *join, yoke, mate*

Iuppiter, Iovis, m., *Jupiter,* supreme god of the Romans, god of sky and weather

iūs, iūris, n., *law, right, court*

iustitia, -ae, f., *justice*

iuvenis, iuvenis, m., (f.), *young man, young woman*

iuvō, iuvāre, iūvī, iūtum, *please, delight, help*

L

lābor, lābī, lapsus sum, *glide, slip, pass*

labor, labōris, m., *work, effort, task*

labōrō, labōrāre, labōrāvī, labōrātum, *work, suffer, labor*

labrum, -ī, n., *lip*

lacerta, -ae, f., *lizard*

lacertus, -ī, m., *upper arm*

laedō, laedere, laesī, laesum, *harm, strike*

laetitia, -ae, f., *happiness, joy*

laetus, -a, -um, adj., *happy, glad, fertile*

Lalagē, Lalagēs, f., *Lalage,* woman's name; Greek for "chatterer"

lambō, lambere, lambī, *lick, wash*

languidus, -a, -um, adj., *languid, sluggish, slow*

lapis, lapidis, m., *stone*

largē, adv., *generously, plentifully*

lascīvus, -a, -um, adj., *playful, frisky, wanton*

lateō, latēre, latuī, *lie hidden*

lātus, -a, -um, adj., *wide*

latus, lateris, n., *side, extreme part or region, flank, lungs, body*

laudō, laudāre, laudāvī, laudātum, *praise*

laurus, -ī/-ūs, f., *laurel tree*

laus, laudis, f., *praise*

lavō, lavāre/lavere, lāvī, lavātum/lautum/lōtum, *wash*

lēnis, -e, adj., *smooth, gentle, mild, soft*

lentus, -a, -um, adj., *slow, lingering, unresponsive*

leō, leōnis, m., *lion*

lepus, leporis, m., *hare, rabbit*

Lesbōus, -a, -um, adj., *Lesbian, of the Greek island of Lesbos*

Lēthaeus, -a, -um, adj., *relating to Lethe or the underworld;* Lethe is a place or river in the underworld whose waters, if drunk, were supposed to induce sleepiness or forgetfulness.

Leuconoē, Leuconoēs, f., *Leuconoe,* woman's name

levis, -e, adj., *light, swift, gentle, unimportant, fickle*

lēvis, -e, adj., *smooth, smooth* (from polishing)

lex, lēgis, f., *law, rule, particular condition or term*

libens, libentis, adj., *willing*

līber, lībera, līberum, adj., *free*

līberō, līberāre, līberāvī, līberātum, *free*

libīdō, libīdinis, f., *desire, lust*

Libitīna, -ae, f., *Libitina,* the goddess of funerals, *funeral couch*

Liburna, -ae, f., *light, fast sailing warship, galley;* name taken from the Liburnians, a people of Illyricum

Libycus, -a, -um, adj., *Libyan,* sometimes *African,* in general

licet, licēre, licuit/licitum est, impersonal verb, *it is permitted*

Licinius, Liciniī, m., *Licinius;* maybe Lucius Licinius Murena, brother-in-law of Maecenas, who was executed when trying to escape after his alleged participation in a conspiracy against Augustus

lignum, -ī, n., *wood* (often in pl.)

līmen, līminis, n., *threshold*

lingua, -ae, f., *tongue, language*

linquō, linquere, līquī, *go away from, abandon, leave behind*

liquidus, -a, -um, adj., *flowing, clear, melodious, liquid*

liquō, liquāre, liquāvī, liquātum, *melt, strain*

līs, lītis, f., *quarrel, lawsuit*

lītus, lītoris, n., *shore, coast, beach*

lituus, lituī, m., *curved cavalry trumpet*

locus, -ī, m., *place, occasion;* m. pl., **-i;** n. pl., **-a**

longē, adv., *far, far off, far away in time*

longus, -a, -um, adj., *long*

loquax, loquācis, adj., *talkative, loquacious, talking*

loquor, loquī, locūtus sum, *speak*

lucrum, -ī, n., *profit, gain*

luctor, luctārī, luctātus sum, *wrestle, struggle, contend*

lūgubris, -e, adj., *mournful*

lūna, -ae, f., *moon*

lupus, -ī, m., *wolf*

Lȳdia, -ae, f., *Lydia,* woman's name

lympha, -ae, f., *water*

lymphātus, -a, -um, adj., *frenzied, distracted, frantic*

lyricus, -a, -um, adj., *of the lyre, lyric*

M

mācerō, mācerāre, mācerāvī, mācerātum, *soften, make weak, torment*

Maecēnās, Maecēnātis, m., *Gaius Cilnius Maecenas,* friend and supporter of Horace and of other contemporary poets, including Vergil

maestus, -a, -um, adj., *sad, sorrowful, dejected, gloomy*

magis, adv., *more*

magnus, -a, -um, adj., *large, big, great*

maior, maius, adj., *greater, larger*

male, adv., *badly, insufficiently, wickedly, scarcely*

mālobathrum, -ī, n., *the tree Cinnamomum tamala or its oil*

malus, -a, -um, adj., *bad, nasty, hostile, unfavorable*

maneō, manēre, mansī, mansum, *remain, stay, endure*

mānō, mānāre, mānāvī, mānātum, *flow, spread*

manus, -ūs, f., *hand, band*

mare, maris, n., *sea*

Mareōticum, -ī, n., *wine from Mareotis,* area around Alexandria in Egypt

Mars, Martis, m., *Mars,* god of war

Marsus, -a, -um, adj., *Marsian, of the* **Marsī,** a people of central Italy

Massicum, -ī, n., *Massic wine, wine from the area of* **Massicus,** a mountain in Campania

Massicus, -a, -um, adj., *Massic*

māter, mātris, f., *mother*

Maurus, -a, -um, adj., *Moorish, African*

mēcum = cum mē

mediocritās, mediocritātis, f., *mean, moderation, keeping of a middle course*

meditor, meditārī, meditātus sum, *think over, contemplate, practice*

melior, melius, adj., *better*

Melpomenē, Melpomenēs, f., *Melpomene,* one of the Muses

membrum, -ī, n., *limb or member of the body, limb, member, part of anything*

meminī, meminisse (perf. with pres. meaning), *remember, recollect*

memor, memoris, adj., *mindful, remembering*

mendax, mendācis, adj., *lying, false*

mens, mentis, f., *mind*

mentum, -ī, n., *chin*

mercātor, mercātōris, m., *merchant*

Mercurius, Mercuriī, m., *Mercury,* son of Jupiter and Maia

meritum, -ī, n., *that which one deserves, due reward, service, meritorious action*

merus, -a, -um, adj., *pure, unmixed;* with **vīnum** or with **vīnum** understood, *wine not mixed with water*

mēta, -ae, f., *turning point, end*

metuō, metuere, metuī, metūtum, *fear, be afraid of, be afraid*

metus, -ūs, m., *fear*

meus, -a, -um, adj., *my*

mī = mihi

mīlitāris, -e, adj., *military*

mīlitia, -ae, f., *military service, war, army*

minae, -ārum, f. pl., *threats, warning signs*

minax, minācis, adj., *threatening, projecting*

minimus, -a, -um, adj., *smallest, least*

minister, ministrī, m., *servant, assistant*

Mīnōs, Mīnōis/Minōnis, m., *Minos,* king of Crete, and later a judge in the underworld

minuō, minuere, minuī, minūtum, *make smaller, reduce, weaken*

minus, adv., *less*

misceō, miscēre, miscuī, mixtum, *mix, mingle*

miser, misera, miserum, adj., *unhappy, pitiful*

miserē, adv., *pitifully, desperately*

miseror, miserārī, miserātus sum, *pity, lament*

mītescō, mītescere, *become mild, soft, or ripe*

mittō, mittere, mīsī, missum, *release, let go, abandon, send*

mōbilis, -e, adj., *moveable, changeable, inconstant, pliant*

moderor, moderārī, moderātus sum, *handle, control, play*

modo, adv., *only, just now*

modus, -ī, m., *limit, way, rhythmic pattern;* in pl., *poetry*

moechus, -ī, m., *adulterer*

mōlēs, mōlis, f., *mass, bulk, massive structure*

mōlior, mōlīrī, mōlītus sum, *labor at, build*

mollis, -e, adj., *soft, gentle, flexible, voluptuous*

moneō, monēre, monuī, monitum, *bring to the notice of, remind, tell (of), warn*

mons, montis, m., *mountain*

monstrum, -ī, n., *portent, marvel, monster*

monumentum, -ī, n., *monument, memorial*

mora, -ae, f., *delay, hindrance*

morbus, -ī, m., *sickness, disease*

morior, morī, mortuus sum, *die*

moror, morārī, morātus sum, *delay, linger, be late in appearing*

mōrōsus, -a, -um, adj., *difficult*

mors, mortis, f., *death*

mortālis, -e, adj., *mortal*

mōs, mōris, m., *custom, tradition;* (pl.) *character, habits*

moveō, movēre, mōvī, mōtum, *move*

mox, adv., *soon*

muliebriter, adv., *like a woman*

mulier, mulieris, f., *woman, wife*

multum, adv., *much*

multus, -a, -um, adj., *much, many, large* (with sing. noun)

munditia, -ae, f., *neatness, elegance*

mundus, -ī, m., *world*

mūnus, mūneris, n., *service, duty, gift, entertainment*

Mūsa, -ae, f., *muse;* one of the nine Muses, goddesses who were daughters of Zeus and Mnemosyne and presided over the arts

mūtō, mūtāre, mūtāvī, mūtātum, *change*

mūtuus, -a, -um, adj., *mutual, reciprocal*

Myrtōus, -a, -um, adj., *Myrtoan*

myrtus, -ī, f., *myrtle*

N

nam, conj., *for, because*

namque, conj., *for, because*

narrō, narrāre, narrāvī, narrātum, *tell*

nascor, nascī, nātus sum, *be born*

nauta, -ae, m., *sailor*

nāvis, nāvis, f., *ship*

nē, negative adv. and conj., *not, that not, so that not, lest;* used in negative purpose clauses and prohibitions, among other constructions

-ne, interr. particle, in direct questions; in indirect questions with alternatives, often used with **an,** *whether . . . or;* affirmative particle often used with infinitive in exclamations, *indeed*

nebula, -ae, f., *mist, fog*

nec, conj., *and not;* **nec . . . nec,** *neither . . . nor*

nectar, nectaris, n., *nectar,* drink of the gods

nectō, nectere, nexī, nexum, *tie, weave, bind, compose*

nefās, n., indecl., *crime, offense against divine law, sacrilege*

negō, negāre, negāvī, negātum, *say no, deny, refuse*

nēmō, nēminis, m., pron., *no one, nobody*

nemus, nemoris, n., *grove, forest*

neque, conj., *and not;* **neque . . . neque,** *neither . . . nor*

nesciō, nescīre, nescīvī, nescītum, *not know, be ignorant of, not to know how to, not to be able to*

nescius, -a, -um, adj., *ignorant, unaware*

niger, nigra, nigrum, adj., *black, dark, gloomy, black as a color of ill omen, evil*

nihil, n., indecl., *nothing*

nīl = nihil

nimium, adv., *too, too much, very*

nisi, conj., *if not, unless*

niteō, nitēre, nituī, *shine, be radiant with beauty*

nivālis, -e, adj., *snowy*

nix, nivis, f., *snow*

nōbilis, -e, adj., *noble*

noceō, nocēre, nocuī, nocitum, *harm* (with dat.)

nōmen, nōminis, n., *name*

nōn, adv., *not*

nōs, nostrī/nostrum, nōbīs, nōs, nōbīs, pron., *we, us*

noscō, noscere, nōvī, nōtum, *get to know learn; know* (in perfect tense)

nota, -ae, f., *mark, sign, wine of a specified quality or vintage*

nōtus, -a, -um, adj., *known, familiar*

novus, -a, -um, adj., *new, strange*

nox, noctis, f., *night*

nūdus, -a, -um, adj., *naked, bare, plain*

nūgae, -ārum, f. pl., *trifles, nonsense, things of no importance*

nullus, -a, -um, adj., *no, not any*

num, interr. particle, *certainly not*

numerus, -ī, m., *number*

numquam, adv., *never*

numquid, interr. particle, introduces question where a negative answer is expected, *surely . . . not; you don't, do you?*

nunc, adv., *now*

nūtō, nūtāre, nūtāvī, nūtātum, *nod with the head, nod, hesitate*

nūtrix, nūtrīcis, f., *nurse, especially a wet-nurse*

nympha, -ae, f., *nymph, semi-divine female spirit of nature*

O

ō, interj., *O* (with voc.)

obeō, obīre, obiī, obitum, *go to, meet, die*

obligō, obligāre, obligāvī, obligātum, *tie up, pledge, dedicate*

oblīquus, -a, -um, adj., *slanting, zigzag*

oblīviōsus, -a, -um, adj., *producing forgetfulness, forgetful*

obsolētus, -a, -um, adj., *worn out, shabby, ordinary*

obstrepō, obstrepere, obstrepuī, obstrepitum, *make a loud, noise, roar, drown by louder noise*

obvius, -a, -um, adj. (with dat.), *in the way, placed so as to meet, situated so as to confront*

occidō, occidere, occidī, occāsum, *fall, die*

occupō, occupāre, occupāvī, occupātum, *seize, forestall, take the lead over*

occurrō, occurrere, occurrī/occucurrī, occursum, *meet, hurry to meet, arrive, turn up*

ōcius, adv., *sooner, quicker*

oculus, -ī, m., *eye*

ōdī, ōdisse, ōsum (perfect with present sense), *have an aversion to, hate*

odor, odōris, m., *smell, odor, perfume*

officiō, officere, offēcī, offectum, *impede, interfere with* (with dat.)

ōlim, adv., *formerly, once, on an occasion, at some future date*

Olympicus, -a, -um, adj., *Olympic, Olympian*

omnis, -e, adj., *all, every*

onus, oneris, n., *burden*

operōsus, -a, -um, adj., *toilsome, laborious, painstaking, industrious*

oppēdō, oppēdere, *fart in the face of* (with dat.)

oppidum, -ī, n., *town*

oppōnō, oppōnere, opposuī, oppositum, *place against, place in front, especially put before someone for acceptance, proffer*

oppositus, -a, -um, *placed against, hostile*

opus, operis, n., *work, business, task, genre;* with **esse,** *be necessary, be needed* (with abl. of thing needed and dat. of person with the need)

ōra, -ae, f., *shore*

Orcus, Orcī, m., *Orcus, the god of the lower world, the lower world, death*

ordinō, ordināre, ordināvī, ordinātum, *set in order, arrange*

orior, orīrī, ortus sum, *rise, be born*

ornō, ornāre, ornāvī, ornātum, *prepare, decorate, adorn, honor* (with abl.)

ornus, -ī, f., *flowering ash tree*

Ornytus, -ī, m., *Ornytus,* man's name

Orpheus, -ī, m., *Orpheus;* he was able to charm animals and nature with his music.

osculum, -ī, n., *kiss, mouth, lips* (as used in kissing)

ōtium, ōtiī, n., *free time, leisure, peace*

P

palma, -ae, f., *palm tree, palm branch, palm wreath, token of victory*

pār, paris, adj., *equal*

parcē, adv., *sparingly*

parcō, parcere, pepercī, parsum, *spare* (with dat.)

pariēs, parietis, m., *wall*

parmula, -ae, f., *little shield*

parō, parāre, parāvī, parātum, *prepare*

pars, partis, f., *part, party; stage role* (usually in pl.)

pateō, patēre, patuī, *be open*

pater, patris, m., *father*

patientia, -ae, f., *patience*

patior, patī, passus sum, *suffer, undergo, experience, endure, allow*

patrius, -a, -um, adj., *of a father, ancestral, native, inherited, belonging to one's country*

paucus, -a, -um, adj., in pl., *few*

paulum, adv., *for a short while*

paulum, -ī, n., *a little*

pauper, pauperis, adj., *poor* (with gen.)

pauperiēs, pauperiēī, f., *poverty*

paveō, pavēre, *be frightened, be terrified*

pavidus, -a, -um, adj., *frightened, terrified, trembling, fearful*

pavīmentum, -ī, n., *pavement, floor*

pectus, pectoris, n., *breast, chest*

pecus, pecoris, n., *farm animal;* sing. as collective, *farm animals, livestock,* especially *sheep and cattle*

pendeō, pendēre, pependī, *hang, hover, hang down, be suspended*

penitus, adv., *deeply*

per, prep. with acc., *through*

perdō, perdere, perdidī, perditum, *destroy, lose*

perennis, -e, adj., *lasting throughout the year, lasting for many years, enduring*

pereō, perīre, periī, peritum, *perish, die*

perfundō, perfundere, perfūdī, perfūsum, *pour over, fill with*

permisceō, permiscēre, permiscuī, permixtum, *mix together, confuse*

permittō, permittere, permīsī, permissum, *let go, allow, entrust*

permūtō, permūtāre, permūtāvī, permūtātum, *exchange, receive in exchange for* (with acc. of thing received and abl. of thing given up)

perpetuus, -a, -um, adj., *continuing, permanent, connected*

Persae, Persārum, m. pl., *Persians*

persequor, persequī, persecūtus sum, *pursue, chase*

Persicus, -a, -um, adj., *Persian*

pertinax, pertinācis, adj., *very tenacious, holding fast, persisting*

pēs, pedis, m., *foot, metrical foot*

petītor, petītōris, m., *seeker, candidate*

pharetra, -ae, f., *quiver*

Philippī, -ōrum, m. pl., *Philippi,* town in eastern Macedonia where Brutus and Cassius were defeated

philyra, -ae, f., *fibrous membrane under the bark of the linden or lime tree, bast;* used to bind together elaborate garlands of flowers

Phrygius, -a, -um, adj., *Phrygian*

pietās, pietātis, f., *duty, devotion*

piger, pigra, pigrum, adj., *inactive, lazy*

pignus, pigneris/pignoris, n., *pledge, token, symbol*

pīnus, -ūs, f., *pine*

Pīrithous, -ī, m., *Pirithous,* a king of the Lapiths who fights with the Centaurs; son by Dia of Zeus or Ixion

piscis, piscis, m., *fish*

pius, -a, -um, adj., *dutiful, devoted*

placeō, placēre, placuī, placitum, *please*

plācō, plācāre, plācāvī, plācātum, *appease, calm*

plaga, -ae, f., *hunting net, trap*

plūs, plūris, n., *more;* **plūrēs, plūra,** pl. adj., *more*

Plūtō, Plūtōnis, m., *Pluto,* king of the underworld

pōculum, -ī, n., *cup, drink*

podagra, -ae, f., *gout*

Polyhymnia, -ae, f., *Polyhymnia,* one of the Muses

pōmifer, pōmifera, pōmiferum, adj., *fruit-bearing, fruitful*

Pompēius, Pompēiī, m., *Pompeius;* identity unknown

pōnō, pōnere, posuī, positum, *put, place*

pontifex, pontificis, m., *high priest, pontiff*

pōpulus, -ī, f., *poplar tree*

populus, -ī, m., *people, public, multitude*

portentum, -ī, n., *portent, abnormal phenomenon*

poscō, poscere, poposcī, *demand*

possum, posse, potuī, *be able, can*

post, prep. with acc., *behind, after*

posterus, -a, -um, adj., *next, following, future, later*

postis, postis, m., *door-post, door*

Postumus, -ī, m., *Postumus;* this name was often given to boys who were born after the death of their fathers

potens, potentis, adj., *able, powerful, potent*

potior, potīrī, potītus sum, *get possession of, obtain, possess*

potior, potius, adj., *more able, more powerful, preferable*

praebeō, praebēre, praebuī, praebitum, *give, supply, provide*

praecēdō, praecēdere, praecessī, praecessum, *go in front, go on ahead*

praecipiō, praecipere, praecēpī, praeceptum, *take beforehand, teach*

praemium, praemiī, n., *prize, reward*

praeparō, praeparāre, praeparāvī, praeparātum, *prepare*

praesidium, praesidiī, n., *protection, defense*

praeter, prep. with acc., *except, beyond*

praetereō, praeterīre, praeteriī, praeteritum, *go by, go past, pass by, go beyond, omit*

premō, premere, pressī, pressum, *press, follow closely*

pressō, pressāre, pressāvī, pressātum, *press*

prex, precis, f., *prayer*

prīmus, -a, -um, adj., *first*

princeps, principis, adj., *first in time, leading, first*

priscus, -a, -um, adj., *ancient, former*

prius, adv., *previously, before*

prīvātus, -a, -um, adj., *private, not in public life*

prō, prep. with abl., *for, on behalf of, in front of*

procella, -ae, f., *storm, trouble*

prōditor, prōditōris, m., *betrayer, traitor*

proelium, proeliī, n., *battle*

profānus, -a, -um, adj., *profane, secular, impious, uninitiated*

prope, prep. with acc., *near*

properō, properāre, properāvī, properātum, *hurry, hasten*

propinquus, -a, -um, adj., *near, neighboring*

proprius, -a, -um, adj., *one's own, personal*

prōterō, prōterere, prōtrīvī, prōtrītum, *trample down, crush*

protervus, -am, -um, adj., *bold, violent*

proxumus, -a, -um, adj., *nearest, next*

pūbēs, pūbis, f., *adult population, age of puberty, the pubic region*

pudīcus, -a, -um, adj., *having a sense of modesty or shame, modest, honorable, chaste*

pudor, pudōris, m., *restraint, feeling of shame*

puella, -ae, f., *girl, young woman, girlfriend*

puer, puerī, m., *boy, non-adult male, male beloved, (young) male slave*

pulcher, pulchra, pulchrum, adj., *beautiful*

pullus, -a, -um, adj., *gray, somber*

pulsō, pulsāre, pulsāvī, pulsātum, *beat, strike repeatedly*

pulvīnar, pulvīnāris, n., *sacred couch on which the image of a god was placed*

pulvis, pulveris, m., *dust*

pūmex, pūmicis, m., *pumice-stone*

purpura, -ae, f., *shellfish yielding a purple dye, the purple dye from the shellfish, purple-dyed cloth, purple*

pūrus, -a, -um, adj., *pure, innocent*

pȳramis, pȳramidis, f., *pyramid*

Pyrrha, -ae, f., *Pyrrha,* woman's name

Q

quā, adv., *where*

quadrīmus, -a, -um, adj., *four-year-old*

quaerō, quaerere, quaesīvī, quaesītum, *look for, seek, ask, acquire, earn*

quālis, -e, rel. adj., *of which sort*

quam, interr. and rel. adv., *how;* with the superlative, *as . . . as possible;* after a comparative, *than*

quamquam, conj., *although*

quandō, interr. adv., *when*

quandōcumque, adv., *at some time or other*

quārē, interr. and rel. adv., *in what way, how, why, because, therefore*

quartus, -a, -um, adj., *fourth*

quatiō, quatere, quassum, *shake, beat upon*

-que, enclitic conj., *and*

querimōnia, -ae, f., *complaint*

questus, -ūs, m., *complaint, lament*

quī, quae, quod, rel. pron., *who, which, that;* interr. adj., *what, which*

quia, conj., *because*

quīcumque, quaecumque, quodcumque, indef. pron., *whoever, whichever, whatever*

quid, adv., *why*

quīdam, quaedam, quiddam, pron., *a certain person, a certain thing*

quīlibet, quaelibet, quidlibet, pron., *anyone or anything whatever, whoever or whatever you please*

Quintilius, Quintiliī, m., *Quintilius Varus,* friend of Horace and Vergil

quintus, -a, -um, adj., *fifth*

Quirīs, Quirītis, m., *Roman citizen*

quis, quid, interr. pron., *who, what;* indef. pron., *anyone, anything*

quisquam, quicquam, pron., *anyone, anything*

quisque, quaeque, quidque, pron., *each one*

quisquis, quidquid (or **quicquid**), pron. and adj., *whoever, whatever*

quō, adv., *where, for what purpose*

quod, conj., *because*

quodsī, conj., *but if*

quōmodo, interr., rel. adv., *how, in the manner in which*

quondam, adv., *once, formerly, sometimes, in the future*

quoque, adv., *also, too*

quotiens, adv., *how often*

quotquot, indecl. adj., *however many*

R

rāmus, -ī, m., *branch*

rapiō, rapere, rapuī, raptum, *seize, snatch away*

ratis, ratis, f., *raft, boat, ship*

raucus, -a, -um, adj., *hoarse, noisy, raucous*

recens, recentis, adj., *fresh, recent, modern*

recipiō, recipere, recēpī, receptum, *take back, accept, regain*

reclīnō, reclīnāre, reclīnāvī, reclīnātum, *cause to lean back*

reclūdō, reclūdere, reclūsī, reclūsum, *open up, undo*

recreō, recreāre, recreāvī, recreātum, *recreate, restore, revive*

rectus, -a, -um, adj., *straight, right, correct, proper*

recurrō, recurrere, recurrī, recursum, *run back, return*

reddō, reddere, reddidī, redditum, *give back, deliver*

redemptor, redemptōris, m., *contractor*

redeō, redīre, rediī, reditum, *go back, come back, return*

redigō, redigere, redēgī, redactum, *drive back, reduce*

redōnō, redōnāre, redōnāvī, redōnātum, *give back*

redūcō, redūcere, reduxī, reductum, *bring back*

reficiō, reficere, refēcī, refectum, *make again, repair*

refugiō, refugere, refūgī, *run away, avoid*

rēgālis, -e, adj., *royal, regal*

rēgia, -ae, f., *palace*

rēgīna, -ae, f., *queen*

regnō, regnāre, regnāvī, regnātum, *rule, rule over*

regō, regere, rexī, rectum, *guide, direct, rule*

rēiciō, rēicere, rēiēcī, rēiectum, *throw back, drive back, reject*

religiō, religiōnis, f., *religious awe or conscience, religious practice, particular set of religious observances, cult, religious feeling, superstition*

religō, religāre, religāvī, religātum, *tie, fasten behind; untie (occasionally)*

relinquō, relinquere, relīquī, relictum, *leave, leave behind, abandon*

removeō, removēre, remōvī, remōtum, *move back*

rēmus, -ī, m., *oar*

reor, rērī, ratus sum, *think*

reparō, reparāre, reparāvī, reparātum, *obtain in exchange for, recover*

repetō, repetere, repetīvī, repetītum, *seek again, recall, resume*

repōnō, repōnere, reposuī, repositum, *put down, place*

rēs, reī, f., *wealth, thing, circumstance, affair, legal matter*

resecō, resecāre, resecuī, resectum, *cut back, prune, restrain*

resorbeō, resorbēre, *suck back, swallow again*

respondeō, respondēre, respondī, responsum, *answer, reply;* technical sense, *appear in court*

restituō, restituere, restituī, restitūtum, *restore, revive*

restō, restāre, restitī, *remain, remain to be dealt with*

rex, rēgis, m., *king*

rīdeō, rīdēre, rīsī, rīsum, *laugh*

rīpa, -ae, f., *bank of a river, shore*

rīsus, -ūs, m., *laughter*

rītus, -ūs, m., *ritual, custom, manner, style*

rīvus, -ī, m., *stream*

rixa, -ae, f., *fight*

rogō, rogāre, rogāvī, rogātum, *ask, ask for*

Rōmānus, -a, -um, adj., *Roman*

rosa, -ae, f., *rose*

roseus, -a, -um, adj., *rosy*

rota, -ae, f., *wheel*

ruber, rubra, rubrum, adj., *red*

rubus, -ī, m., *bramble, prickly bush*

rūga, -ae, f., *wrinkle*

ruīna, -ae, f., *collapse, ruin*

rumpō, rumpere, rūpī, ruptum, *break, shatter, destroy*

rursus, adv., *back, again*

rūs, rūris, n., *the country* (as opposed to the town), *farm, estate*

S

sabbata, sabbatōrum, n. pl., *the Jewish sabbath*

Sabellus, -a, -um, adj., *Sabine;* the Sabines were a people of central Italy.

Sabīnus, -a, -um, adj., *Sabine;* the Sabines were a people of central Italy.

sacer, sacra, sacrum, adj., *sacred, holy*

sacerdōs, sacerdōtis, c., *priest or priestess*

saepe, adv., *often*

saeviō, saevīre, saeviī, saevītum, *rage, rave*

saevus, -a, -um, adj., *cruel, savage*

sagitta, -ae, f., *arrow*

Saliāris, -e, adj., *of the Salii,* who were a group of priests (at Rome usually associated with Mars), who performed ritual dances on certain occasions.

salsus, -a, -um, adj., *salted, witty, funny*

saltus, -ūs, m., *forest or mountain pasture, forest or mountain pass*

salvus, -a, -um, adj., *safe, alive, well*

sanguis, sanguinis, m., *blood*

sānus, -a, -um, adj., *healthy, sane*

sapienter, adv., *wisely*

sapiō, sapere, sapīvī, *have taste, be wise*

sapor, sapōris, m., *taste, flavor*

sarculum, -ī, n., *hoe*

satis, adv., *enough, sufficiently;* indecl. noun, *enough*

Satyrus, -ī, m., *satyr;* demi-god of wild places, especially forests, having the form of a man with some animal characteristics

saxum, -ī, n., *rock*

scandō, scandere, *climb, ascend, mount*

scelus, sceleris, n., *wrongdoing, crime, affliction*

scīlicet, adv., *evidently, of course, surely*

sciō, scīre, scīvī, scītum, *know*

scrībō, scrībere, scripsī, scriptum, *write*

sēcernō, sēcernere, sēcrēvī, sēcrētum, *separate, distinguish*

secō, secāre, secuī, sectum, *cut, divide, traverse*

sēcrētō, adv., *secretly*

sector, sectārī, sectātus sum, *pursue, chase*

secundus, -a, -um, adj., *following, second, favorable*

secus, adv., *otherwise, not so*

sed, conj., *but*

sedeō, sedēre, sēdī, sessum, *sit*

sēdēs, sēdis, f., *seat, site, home*

sēdulus, -a, -um, adj., *attentive, diligent*

semel, adv., *once, once and for all*

semper, adv., *always*

senecta, -ae, f., *old age*

sentiō, sentīre, sensī, sensum, *feel, sense, perceive, think, understand*

sequor, sequī, secūtus sum, *follow*

serēnus, -a, -um, adj., *calm*

seriēs, (-ēī), f., *series, sequence, succession*

sērius, adv., *later*

serpens, serpentis, m., f., *snake, serpent*

sērus, -a, -um, adj., *late, blossoming after the normal time*

servō, servāre, servāvī, servātum, *keep, protect, save*

servus, -ī, m., *slave*

seu, conj., *or if,* **seu . . . seu,** *whether . . . or*

sī, conj., *if*

sīc, adv., *so, thus, in this way*

Siculus, -a, -um, adj., *Sicilian*

sīcut, adv., *just as, as*

sīdus, sīderis, n., *star; sky* (pl.)

silva, -ae, f., *forest*

similis, -e, adj., *similar, like*

simplex, simplicis, adj., *simple, artless, plain*

simul, conj., *as soon as* (also with **atque**); adv., *at the same time, together*

sine, prep. with abl., *without*

Sīsyphus, -ī, m., *Sisyphus*; son of Aeolus, committed various crimes and is punished in the underworld by forever having to roll a rock up a steep hill only to have it roll down again

situs, -ūs, m., *site*

situs, -ūs, m., *deterioration, neglect*

sīve, conj., *or if,* **sīve . . . sīve,** *whether . . . or*

sōbrius, -a, -um, adj., *sober, moderate, sensible*

sodālis, sodālis, m., *companion*

sōl, sōlis, m., *sun, a day* (as determined by the rising of the sun)

soleō, solēre, solitus sum, *be accustomed*

solidus, -a, -um, adj., *solid, complete, entire*

sollicitō, sollicitāre, sollicitāvī, sollicitātum, *rouse, excite, shake up, disturb with repeated attacks*

solum, -ī, n., *ground, floor, land*

sōlus, -a, -um, adj., *alone, lonely, deserted*

solvō, solvere, solvī, solūtum, *loosen, break up*

somnus, -ī, m., *sleep*

sonitus, -ūs, m., *sound*

sopor, sopōris, m., *sleep*

Sōracte, Sōractis, n., *Soracte,* mountain in the south of Etruria

sordēs, sordis, f., often used in pl., *dirt, squalor, baseness*

soror, sorōris, f., *sister*

sors, sortis, f., *lot, share*

sortior, sortīrī, sortītus sum, *cast lots over, choose*

sospes, sospitis, adj., *safe and sound, unhurt*

spatium, spatiī, n., *space, period of time*

spernō, spernere, sprēvī, sprētum, *remove, reject, scorn*

spērō, spērāre, spērāvī, spērātum, *hope, hope for, expect*

spēs, speī, f., *hope*

splendidus, -a, -um, adj., *bright, brilliant, glittering, illustrious*

sternō, sternere, strāvī, strātum, *stretch out, spread out, level, overthrow*

stō, stāre, stetī, statum, *stand*

suāviter, adv., *pleasantly, delightfully, nicely*

sub, prep. with acc. or abl., *under, below*

subeō, subīre, subiī, subitum, *go under, undergo*

sublīmis, -e, adj., *high, raised, elevated, sublime, lofty*

submoveō, submovēre, submōvī, submōtum, *move away, remove, ward off, banish*

subolēs, subolis, f., *offspring*

sūdor, sūdōris, m., *sweat*

sulcus, -ī, m., *a furrow, trench, track*

sum, esse, fuī, futūrus, *be*

summa, -ae, f., *sum, the whole*

summoveō = submoveō

summus, -a, -um, adj., *highest, topmost*

sūmō, sūmere, sumpsī, sumptum, *take, take on*

super, prep. with abl., *above*

superbia, -ae, f., *pride, arrogance*

superbus, -a, -um, adj., *proud, arrogant*

supercilium, superciliī, n., *eyebrow, nod*

superstes, superstitis, adj., *standing over, surviving*

superus, -a, -um, adj., *upper, higher*

suprēmus, -a, -um, adj., *last, final*

surgō, surgere, surrexī, surrectum, *get up, rise* (of heavenly bodies)

suscitō, suscitāre, suscitāvī, suscitātum, *rouse, awaken*

suspendō, suspendere, suspendī, suspensum, *hang up*

sustineō, sustinēre, sustinuī, sustentum, *hold up, support, withstand*

susurrus, -ī, m., *whispering*

suus, -a, -um, third person reflex. adj., *his, her, its, their* (own)

Syrius, -a, -um, adj., *Syrian*

Syrtis, Syrtis, f., *Syrtis* (especially pl.), name of two areas of sandy flats on the coast between Carthage and Cyrene; whole desert region next to this coast.

T

tabula, -ae, f., *board, plank, writing tablet,* (votive) *tablet*

taceō, tacēre, tacuī, tacitum, *be silent*

tacitus, -a, -um, adj., *silent*

tālus, -ī, m., *ankle bone, ankle, knuckle bone used in games*

tam, adv., *so*

tamen, adv., *nevertheless*

tandem, *at last, finally*

tangō, tangere, tetigī, tactum, *touch*

tantum, adv., *so much, only*

tantummodo, adv., *only*

tardus, -a, -um, adj., *slow, late, moving slowly, dull*

taurus, -ī, m., *bull*

tectum, -ī, n., *roof, house*

tēcum = cum tē

Tēlephus, -ī, m., *Telephus,* man's name

tellūs, tellūris, f., *land, earth, country, ground*

Tempē, n. pl. *Tempe,* valley of the Peneus river between Ossa and Olympus in Thessaly noted for its beauty; *any beautiful valley*

temperō, temperāre, temperāvī, temperātum, *moderate, hold back*

tempestīvus, -a, -um, adj., *timely, seasonable, ripe*

temptō, temptāre, temptāvī, temptātum, *try, attempt*

tempus, temporis, n., *time, occasion, proper time, an age or particular period in history, danger*

tendō, tendere, tetendī, tentum/tensum, *stretch out, extend, proceed, direct one's course*

tenebrae, -ārum, f. pl., *darkness*

teneō, tenēre, tenuī, tentum, *hold, persist*

tener, tenera, tenerum, adj., *tender, delicate, soft, young*

ter, adv., *three times*

teres, teretis, adj., *rounded, smooth, polished*

tergeminus, -a, -um, adj., *triple*

terminus, -ī, m., *boundary line, limit*

terra, -ae, f., *land, ground, country*

Thaliarchus, -ī, m., *Thaliarchus,* Greek man's name

Thēseus, Thēseī/Thēseos, m., *Theseus,* son of Aegeus or Poseidon; national hero of Athens

Thrācius, -a, -um, adj., *Thracian*

Thrēicius, -a, -um, adj., *Thracian*

Thressa, -ae, f., a *Thracian woman;* as fem. adj., *Thracian*

Thūrīnus, -a, -um, adj., *pertaining to the town of Thurii in southern Italy*

Tiberis, Tiberis, m., *the river Tiber*

tībia, -ae, f., *shin bone, tibia, pipe, flute*

tigris, tigris/tigridis, f., *tiger*

timeō, timēre, timuī, *fear, be afraid, be afraid of*

timor, timōris, m., *fear*

tinguō, tinguere, tinxī, tinctum, *wet, stain*

Tityos, -ī, m., *Tityus;* giant primarily known for attempting to rape Latona, mother of Apollo and Diana; punished in the underworld by being stretched over nine acres while two vultures or snakes ate his heart or liver

tollō, tollere, sustulī, sublātum, *lift, raise, extol, take away, destroy*

Torquātus, -ī, m., *Torquatus;* identity uncertain; a Torqutus, an orator, also appears as addressee of Horace *Epistle* 1.5; an orator; may be a son of Lucius Manlius Torquatus, consul in 65 BCE, the year in which Horace was born

torreō, torrēre, torruī, tostum, *burn, parch*

tōtus, -a, -um, adj., *the whole of, all*

trabs, trabis, f., *beam of wood, trunk of tree, ship*

tractō, tractāre, tractāvī, tractātum, *handle*

trādō, trādere, trādidī, trāditum, *hand over, deliver, introduce*

trans, prep. with acc., *across*

trecēnī, trecēnae, trecēna, pl. adj., *three hundred each, three hundred at a time*

tremō, tremere, tremuī, *tremble, quiver*

trepidō, trepidāre, trepidāvī, trepidātum, *be agitated, hurry*

trēs, tria, adj., *three*

tribuō, tribuere, tribuī, tribūtum, *allot, assign*

trīcēsimus, -a, -um, adj., *thirtieth*

trirēmis, trirēmis, f., *ship having three banks of oars; trireme*

tristis, -e, adj., *sad*

triumphus, -ī, m., *triumph, triumphal procession*

trivium, triviī, n., *meeting place of three roads, crossroads*

tū, tuī, tibi, tē, tē, pron., *you* (sing.)

tuba, -ae, f., *straight war trumpet*

Tullus, -ī, m., *Tullus Hostilius,* third king of Rome

tum, adv., *then*

tumeō, tumēre, tumuī, *swell*

tumultuōsus, -a, -um, adj., *full of commotion, turbulent*

tunc, adv., *then*

turba, -ae, f., *crowd*

turgidus, -a, -um, adj., *swollen, turgid*

turpis, -e, adj., *ugly, shameful, disgraceful*

turpō, turpāre, turpāvī, turpātum, *make ugly*

turris, -is, f., *tower*

tussis, tussis, f., *cough*

tūtus, -a, -um, adj., *safe, secure*

tuus, -a, -um, adj., *your* (sing.)

Tyrrhēnus, -a, -um, adj., *Tyrrhenian, Etruscan*

U

ubi, rel. adv., *where, when;* interr. adv., *where*

ūdus, -a, -um, adj., *wet, pliant*

ulcerōsus, -a, -um, adj., *full of ulcers or sores*

ullus, -a, -um, adj., *any*

ultimus, -a, -um, adj., *last, farthest, extreme*

ultrā, prep. with acc., *beyond*

umbra, -ae, f., *shade, shadow, ghost*

umbrōsus, -a, -um, adj., *shady*

umerus, -ī, m., *shoulder*

ūmor, ūmōris, m., *moisture, liquid*

unda, -ae, f., *wave, water*

unde, interr. and rel. adv., *from where, from whom, from which*

undique, adv., *on all sides, everywhere*

unguentum, -ī, n., *ointment, perfume*

ūnus, -a, -um, adj., *one, sole*

urbs, urbis, f., *city; the city of Rome*

urgeō, urgēre, ursī, *push, press upon*

urna, -ae, f., *urn*

ūrō, ūrere, ussī, ustum, *burn;* in pass., *be on fire*

usque, adv., *continuously, continually, all the way*

ūsus, -ūs, m., *use, enjoyment*

ut, conj. with indic., *as, like, when, considering how;* with subj., *so that, that, to;* interr. adv., *how*

ūtor, ūtī, ūsus sum (with abl.), *use, enjoy*

utrimque, adv., *on both sides*

ūvidus, -a, -um, *wet*

uxor, uxōris, f., *wife*

V

vacuus, -a, -um, adj., *empty, free, available*

vador, vadārī, vadātus sum, (of a plaintiff) *accept a guarantee from the other party that the party will appear or reappear in court at an appointed date*

vae, interj., *alas, woe*

vagor, vagārī, vagātus sum, *wander*

vagus, -a, -um, adj., *roaming, wandering*

valeō, valēre, valuī, valitum, *be powerful, be strong enough to, be well*

vallēs, vallis, f., *valley*

vānus, -a, -um, adj., *empty, groundless, imaginary*

Varius, Variī, m., *L.Varius Rufus,* writer of epic and tragedy, important literary friend of Horace

vātēs, vātis, c., *prophet, singer, poet*

-ve, conj., *or*

vel, conj., *or*

vellō, vellere, vellī, vulsum, *pull, tug at*

vēlum, -ī, n., *sail*

velut, adv., *as, just as*

vēnātor, vēnātōris, m., *hunter*

venēnātus, -a, -um, adj., *poisonous*

venēnum, -ī, n., *poison, magical or medicinal potion*

veniō, venīre, vēnī, ventum, *come*

ventus, -ī, m., *wind*

venus, veneris, f., *Venus,* Roman goddess of love; *love, charm, sexual activity; best throw at dice*

vēr, vēris, n., *spring*

verberō, verberāre, verberāvī, verberātum, *beat, lash*

Vergilius, Vergiliī, m., *Publius Vergilius Maro (70–19 BCE)*

vēritās, vēritātis, f., *truth*

vērō, adv., *in fact, indeed, certainly, truly*

verrō, verrere, versum, *sweep together, collect*

versō, versāre, versāvī, versātum, *keep turning, stir*

versus, -ūs, m., *line of verse*

vertex, verticis, m., *head, summit*

vērus, -a, -um, adj., *true, real*

vescor, vescī, *enjoy, feed on, eat* (with abl.)

Vesta, -ae, f., *Vesta,* Roman goddess of the domestic hearth; *temple or shrine of Vesta*

vestīmentum, -ī, n., *clothes, garments*

vetus, veteris, adj., *old*

via, -ae, f., *road, street, way*

vicis (gen.), f., *turn, succession, alternation*

victima, -ae, f., *victim, sacrifice*

victor, victōris, m., *victor, winner, conqueror*

vīcus, -ī, m., *group of dwellings, village; block of houses, street, group of streets,* often forming a social or administrative unit (used of specific districts in Rome)

videō, vidēre, vīdī, vīsum, *see*

vigeō, vigēre, viguī, *flourish, thrive*

villa, -ae, f., *country-house, estate, farm*

vincō, vincere, vīcī, victum, *conquer, defeat*

vinculum, -ī, n., *chain, bond*

vīnea, -ae, f., *vineyard*

vīnum, -ī, n., *wine*

violens, violentis, adj., *violent, vehement*

vir, -ī, m., *man, husband*

vireō, virēre, viruī, *be green, youthful, fresh*

virga, -ae, f., *staff, wand*

virgō, virginis, f., *girl of marriageable age, young woman, virgin*

viridis, -e, adj., *green, fresh, young*

virtūs, virtūtis, f., *manhood, courage, valor, virtue*

Viscus, -ī, m., *Viscus;* there were two brothers with this name; both were literary figures and friends of Horace and Maecenas.

vīsō, vīsere, vīsī, *look at, go and see*

vīta, -ae, f., *life*

vītis, vītis, f., *vine*

vītō, vītāre, vītāvī, vītātum, *avoid, shun*

vitrum, -ī, n., *glass*

vīvō, vīvere, vixī, victum, *live*

vix, adv., *hardly, scarcely*

volens, volentis, adj., *willing*

volgus, -ī, n., *the common people, the general public, crowd*

volō, velle, voluī, *wish, want, be willing*

volō, volāre, volāvī, volātum, *fly, speed*

voltus, -ūs, m., *face, expression*

vōmer, vōmeris, m., *plowshare;* by metonymy, *the plow*

vōtīva, -a, -um, *votive, relating to a vow*

vox, vōcis, f., *voice*

Z

Zephyrus, -ī, m., *west wind, zephyr*

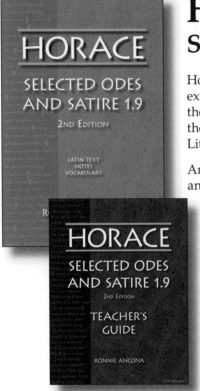